Master the Manual

A Study Guide to Accompany the
ACE Personal Trainer Manual

5820 Oberlin Drive, Suite 102, San Diego, California 92121, 800-825-3636, www.acefitness.org

Printed in the United States of America.

ISBN 0-9618161-8-X

C D E F

Distributed by:
American Council on Exercise
P.O. Box 910449
San Diego, CA 92191-0449
(619) 535-8227
(619) 535-1778 (FAX)
http://www.acefitness.org

Author: Richard J. Seibert
Editor: Richard T. Cotton
Associate Editor: Christine J. Ekeroth
Assistant Editor: Holly Yancy
Design: Grace Anne Swanson
Production: Michael Klepper
Production Assistant: Bryan Cochran
Technical Consultants: Lisa Garrity, Kathleen Hargarten, M.D., Tony Ordas, David Stotlar, Ph.D.
Anatomical Illustrations: James Staunton
Proofreader: Trish Donohue
Chapter Models: Bryan Cochran, Diane Duray-Stoner, Kristen Edwards, Scott Fischer, Melissa Garner, Nancy Heyne, Sandra Leichliter, Tony Ordas, Christopher Ranck-Buhr, Darlene Ravelo, Theresa Schoppe, Holli Spicer, Karen Kay Spicer, Dan Trone
Photography: Rick Starkman

Table of Contents

How to Use this Study Guide

Welcome to *Master the Manual,* a study guide designed as a companion to the *ACE Personal Trainer Manual.* The exercises in this book will help you master the basics of personal training by breaking them into manageable concepts that you can then apply to real-life situations.

Each chapter of the study guide is divided into sections. ***Getting Started*** introduces you to the material, providing objectives and vocabulary words to concentrate on as you read the corresponding chapter in the manual. ***Expand Your Knowledge*** will test your comprehension through a variety of exercises and drills. ***Show What You Know*** exercises your ability to apply what you have learned to real-life situations. Some chapters will take you one step further, providing activities to further expand your skills in ***Practice What You Know***. If you are using the *ACE Personal Trainer Manual* in conjunction with this study guide to prepare for the ACE Personal Trainer Certification Examination, you should focus not only on learning the concepts, but also on applying them to practical training situations. Follow these steps to help you get the most from *Master the Manual.*

Step One: Read

Read the student objectives for each chapter, then read the corresponding chapter in the *ACE Personal Trainer Manual.* Read one chapter at a time rather than attempting to read the entire manual at one sitting. As you read, look for the vocabulary words listed at the beginning of each study guide chapter. When you come across one, mark it in your text.

Step Two: Define

After you have read each chapter and marked the vocabulary words, define each of the words on a separate piece of paper. Write the definition even if you feel you already know it. Learning is a sensory experience, so the more senses you can involve in the learning process, the more you will be able to retain. Writing down definitions, or putting your thoughts into words, will help you to remember the material more clearly.

Step Three: Exercises

After defining the vocabulary words, skim the chapter in the manual again. Attempt to do the exercises in the study guide without looking at the manual. Check your answers against the key that appears in Appendix B, which begins on page 122. If you answer a question incorrectly, go back to the text and find out why your answer is wrong. Make a note to yourself for future reference. If you correctly answered a question, but feel you were guessing, go back to the manual and read that section again. Don't assume you'll remember it.

Step Four: Final Notes

Now is the time to go back to the objectives on the first page of each study guide chapter. Mark any areas you are unsure of or want to learn more about, and reread the related sections in the manual. Refer to the references and suggested reading lists at the end of each manual chapter to find sources for more information.

The focus of this study guide is on learning and retention. That is why we do not grade the exercises or relate the results to either a score, or to your chance for success on the ACE exam. No textbook or study guide can predict your performance on a certification examination. If you feel you need additional preparation, you may call ACE to get information on ACE exam preparation training programs.

CHAPTER

1 Exercise Physiology

Getting Started

This chapter describes the relevant changes in the cells and tissues of the body that occur during the onset of exercise, and the long-term physical adaptations your client can expect from an exercise program. After completing this section you will have a better understanding of:

- the components necessary to achieve optimal fitness
- the physiology of the cardiopulmonary system
- the three energy pathway systems
- the cardiopulmonary responses to exercise and aerobic training
- the four variables to consider when developing a cardiovascular training program
- basic skeletal muscle anatomy and physiology
- the physiological adaptations to strength training
- strength training guidelines
- basic flexibility training

Vocabulary

- specificity training
- optimal physical fitness
- systolic blood pressure
- diastolic blood pressure
- hyperventilation
- contractile proteins
- VO_2 max
- cardiac output
- heart rate
- stroke volume
- ejection fraction
- adenosine triphosphate (ATP)
- creatine phosphate system
- aerobic energy systems
- anaerobic energy systems
- ischemia
- anaerobic threshold
- kilocalorie
- hyperventilation
- enzymes
- metabolic equivalent (MET)
- overload principle
- motor units
- hypertrophy
- nervous inhibition
- cross bridge
- mitochondria
- glycogen
- golgi tendon organ
- muscle spindle

Reading Assignment

Read Chapter 1 of the *ACE Personal Trainer Manual,* paying special attention to the words listed in the box to the left. After you have read the chapter, define these words on a separate piece of paper.

Expand Your Knowledge

I. Match the components of optimal fitness on the right to the definitions on the left.

a. ______ the number of repeated contractions a muscle or muscle group can perform against a resistance without fatiguing

b. ______ the maximum amount of force a muscle or muscle group can develop during a single contraction

c. ______ the ability of the heart, blood and lungs to deliver an adequate supply of oxygen to exercising muscles

d. ______ the sum of fat weight and fat-free weight

e. ______ the amount of movement that can be accomplished at a joint

1. cardiorespiratory endurance
2. muscular strength
3. muscular endurance
4. flexibility
5. body composition

II. Place the following steps in the pattern of blood flow through the heart in order. Begin the pattern at the step where blood discharges CO_2 and binds to O_2 in the lungs.

a. ______ blood discharges O_2 and binds to CO_2 in the body

b. ______ blood enters the right side of the heart

c. ______ blood enters the left side of the heart

d. ______ blood enters the systemic veins

e. ______ blood enters the systemic arteries

f. ______ blood enters the pulmonary arteries

g. ______ blood enters the pulmonary veins

III. Explain the major differences between the following terms.

a. absolute strength gains in men and absolute strength gains in women

____

____

b. pulmonary circulation and systemic circulation

____

____

c. aerobic energy systems and anaerobic energy systems

____

____

d. performance interval training and fitness interval training

____

____

e. slow-twitch muscle fibers and fast-twitch muscle fibers

____

____

f. cardiac muscle and skeletal muscle

____

____

g. immediate muscle soreness and delayed onset muscle soreness

____

____

____

IV. Fill in the space to the right of each letter by placing an (I) if there is an increase, a (D) if there is a decrease, and (NC) if there is no change during a single bout of exercise. Your response is based on a healthy individual and, in some cases, more than one response may be appropriate.

____

a. ______ systolic blood pressure

b. ______ diastolic blood pressure

c. ______ blood flow to the abdominal area

d. ______ amount of peripheral resistance in the vascular system

e. ______ ATP production

V. Describe the primary cause of muscle fatigue in the following three cases.

a. performing a power event or other maximum effort that lasts 0 to 30 seconds

____

____

b. 30 minutes of heavy exercise ______________________________

____

c. running a marathon in three hours ______________________________

____

VI. Fill in the blanks.

a. A healthy body-fat percentage falls in the range of ______ percent to ______ percent for women and ______ percent to ______ percent for men.

b. The rhythmic squeezing action of large muscles against the veins within these muscles is called the ______________________.

c. The ejection fraction is ________ percent at rest and can increase to ________ percent during exercise.

d. Anaerobic threshold is reached somewhere between ______ percent and ______ percent of maximal effort.

e. Optimum exercise intensity for fitness improvements is in the range of ______ percent and ______ percent of maximum heart rate.

VII. List the four factors that limit flexibility.

1. ____

____

2. ____

____

3. ____

____

4. ____

____

VIII. Fill in the space to the right of each letter by placing an (I) if there is an increase, a (D) if there is a decrease, and (NC) if there is no change as a result of aerobic training. Your response is based on a healthy individual and, in some cases, more than one response may be appropriate.

a. ______ resting heart rate

b. ______ stroke volume at rest

c. ______ VO_2 max

d. ______ maximum heart rate

e. ______ mitochondrial density found in muscle

f. ______ anaerobic threshold

g. ______ heart rate at submaximum intensity

IX. Calculate cardiac output max and oxygen extraction max given the following information:
Age: 50
Weight: 75 kg
Max HR: 180 bpm
Max SV: 125 ml/beat
VO_2 max: 48 ml/kg/min

Cardiac output max ____________________________________

O_2 extraction max ____________________________________

X. List the four training rules to follow when developing a cardiovascular fitness program.

1.

2.

3.

4.

XI. List the steps necessary for muscle to contract according to the sliding filament theory.

Show What You Know

I. A client, Eileen, has just started an exercise program that includes strength training. She makes large initial gains in strength after the first three weeks. State why Eileen has made such progress.

II. One of your clients, Anita Brach, is taking a trip around the world. She plans on hiking in three different types of extreme environments: altitude, heat and cold. List some of the potential problems Anita might face in these environments and basic precautions she may take to avoid them.

Practice What You Know

Calculate the average time you spend on each of the five components of optimal fitness each week.

CHAPTER **2** *Human Anatomy*

Getting Started

This chapter describes the structure and function of five major systems within the human body: the cardiovascular system, the respiratory system, the nervous system, the skeletal system and the muscular system. After completing this section you will have a better understanding of:

- basic anatomical terminology
- the functional anatomy of the heart
- the major arteries and veins
- the general phases of respiration
- the central and peripheral nervous systems
- the axial and appendicular skeletal system
- the structure and type of movements allowed by joints
- fundamental movements of the human body
- muscle names and locations

Vocabulary

- anterior
- posterior
- arteries
- veins
- arterioles
- capillaries
- venules
- atrium
- ventricles
- bronchioles
- collagen
- connective tissue
- amenorrhea
- articulation
- ligaments
- axis of rotation
- tendons
- aponeurosis
- agonist
- antagonist
- synergist
- laterally
- proximal
- medial
- distal

Reading Assignment

Read Chapter 2 of the *ACE Personal Trainer Manual,* paying special attention to the words listed in the box to the left. After you have read the chapter, define these words on a separate piece of paper.

Expand Your Knowledge

I. Match the anatomical, directional and regional terms on the right to their descriptions on the left.

a. ______ divides the body into anterior and posterior parts

b. ______ external; located close to or on the surface

c. ______ toward the midline of the body

d. ______ toward the front

e. ______ toward the attached end of the limb, origin of the structure, or midline of the body

f. ______ divides the body, or any of its parts, into superior and inferior sections

g. ______ divides the body, or any of its parts, into right and left sections

h. ______ toward the head

1. anterior
2. superficial
3. superior
4. proximal
5. medial
6. frontal plane
7. sagittal plane
8. transverse plane

II. Aside from distributing oxygen and nutrients to the cells, list the other major functions of the cardiovascular system.

1. ______________________________

____

2. ______________________________

____

3. ______________________________

____

4. ______________________________

____

III. List the artery or vein that carries blood to and from the following sites.

a. dural sinuses to the subclavian vein ______________________

b. to the legs from the external iliac artery ______________________

c. to the arms from the aortic arch ______________________

d. to the heart from the lungs ______________________

e. to the heart from the right and left brachiocephalic veins ____________

f. to the kidneys from the abdominal aorta ______________________

IV. Label the following diagram of the heart, placing the name of the structure to the ***RIGHT*** *of the letter. Place a number to the* ***LEFT*** *of the letter to indicate chronological order of blood flow beginning with blood entering through the superior and inferior vena cava.*

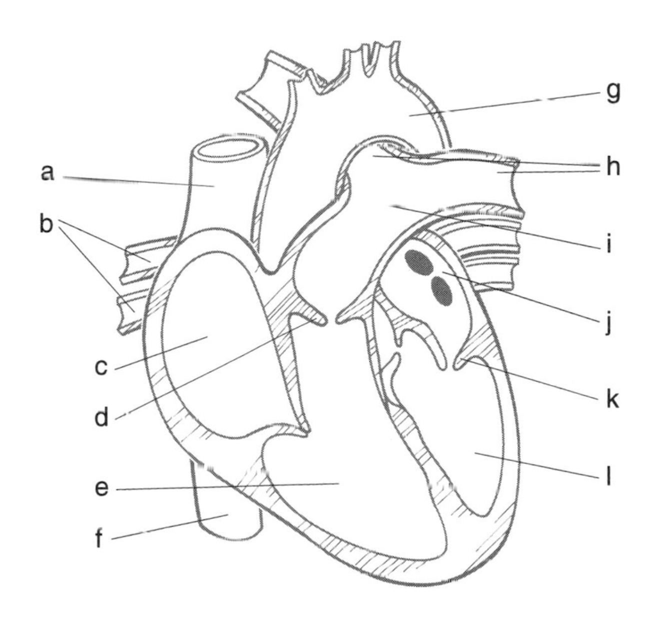

____ a ______________________	____ g ______________________
____ b ______________________	____ h ______________________
____ c ______________________	____ i ______________________
____ d ______________________	____ j ______________________
____ e ______________________	____ k ______________________
____ f ______________________	____ l ______________________

V. Describe the three general phases of respiration.

1. ______________________________

____

____

2. ______________________________

____

____

3. ______________________________

____

____

VI. Number the following steps in the process of oxygen delivery to the capillaries of the lungs, in order, beginning as oxygen is taken into the mouth and nose.

a. _____ through the pharynx

b. _____ oxygen enters the lungs

c. _____ through the primary bronchi

d. _____ through the trachea

e. _____ through the bronchioles

f. _____ through the larynx

g. _____ through the secondary bronchi

h. _____ alveolar ducts

VII. Describe the major differences between the following pairs of words or phrases.

a. central nervous system and peripheral nervous system

b. the axial skeleton and the appendicular skeleton

c. formed elements and plasma

d. skeletal muscle and both cardiac and visceral muscle

e. arteries and veins

VIII. Describe the areas of the body that each of the following nerve branch networks supply.

a. cervical plexus ______________________________

____

b. brachial plexus ______________________________

____

c. lumbar plexus ______________________________

____

d. sacral plexus ______________________________

____

IX. Determine whether the following bones are examples of long bones (L), short bones (S), flat bones (F), or irregular bones (I).

a. _____ scapulae

b. _____ thoracic vertebrae

c. _____ tarsals

d. _____ metatarsals

e. _____ carpals

f. _____ ribs

g. _____ tibia

h. _____ radius

X. Describe the major characteristics of the following joint categories.

a. synovial ______________________________

____

b. cartilaginous ______________________________

____

c. fibrous ______________________________

____

XI. *Name the type and describe the possible movements of the following joints.*

a. thumb ______

______

b. hip ______

______

c. knee ______

______

d. elbow ______

______

e. metacarpophalangeal ______

______

XII. Identify the muscles on the following illustrations as indicated.

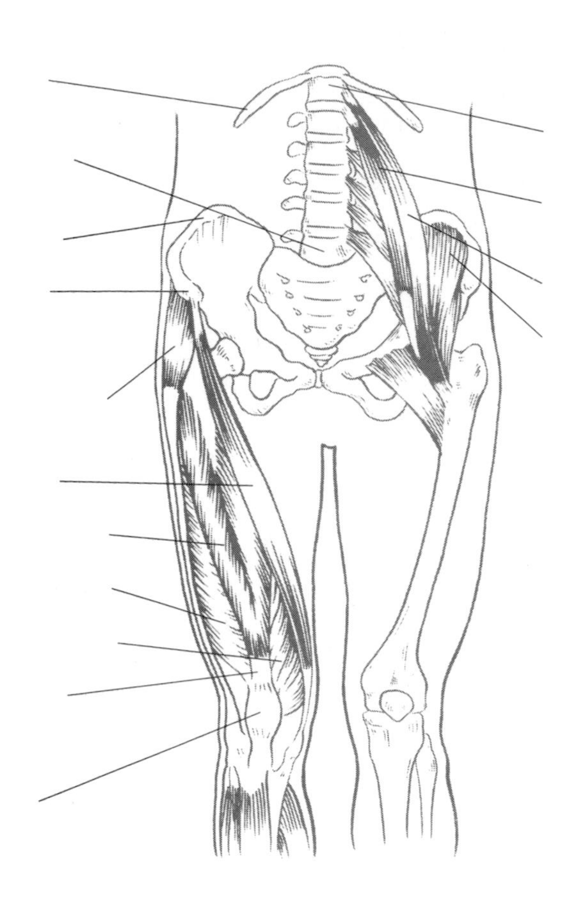

Identify the muscles on the following illustrations as indicated.

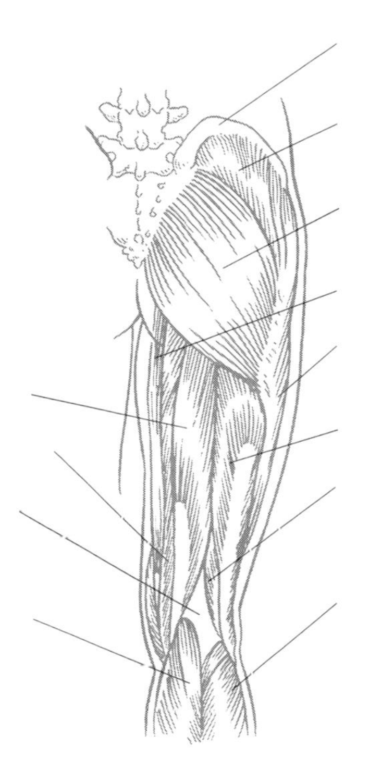

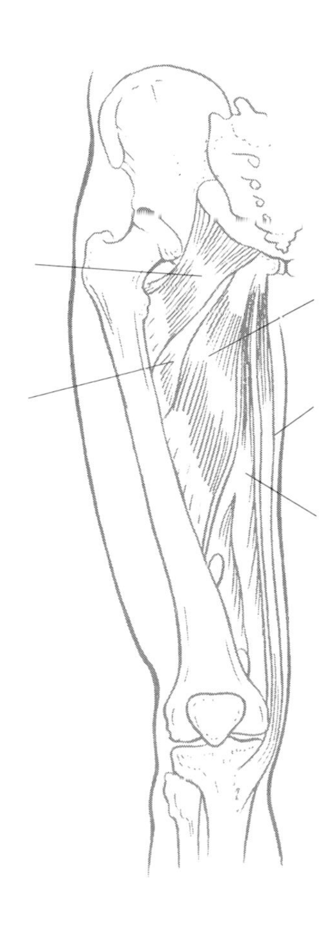

Identify the muscles on the following illustrations as indicated.

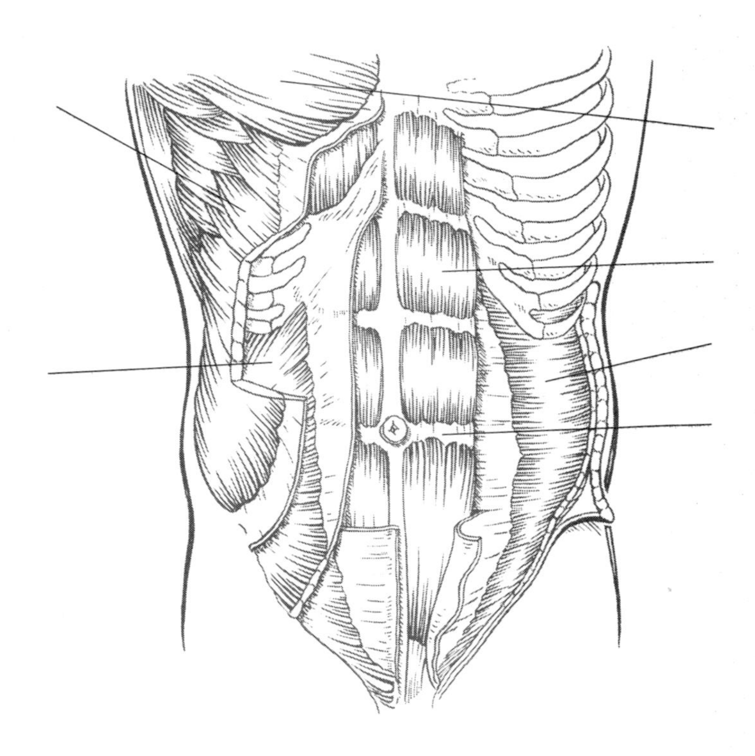

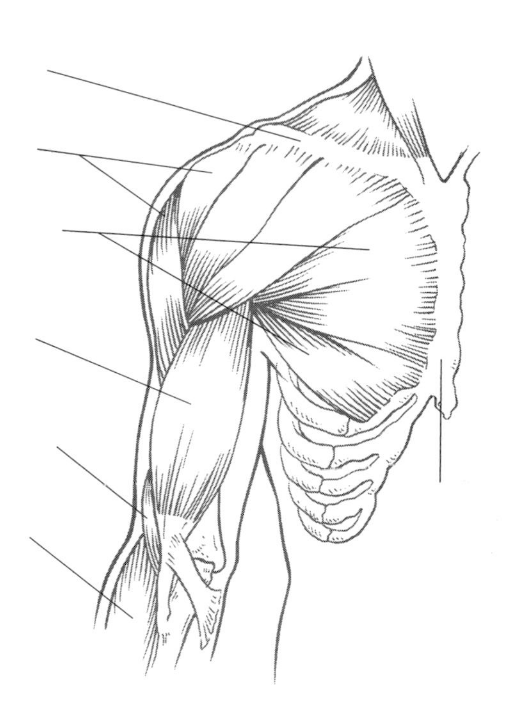

Identify the muscles on the following illustration as indicated.

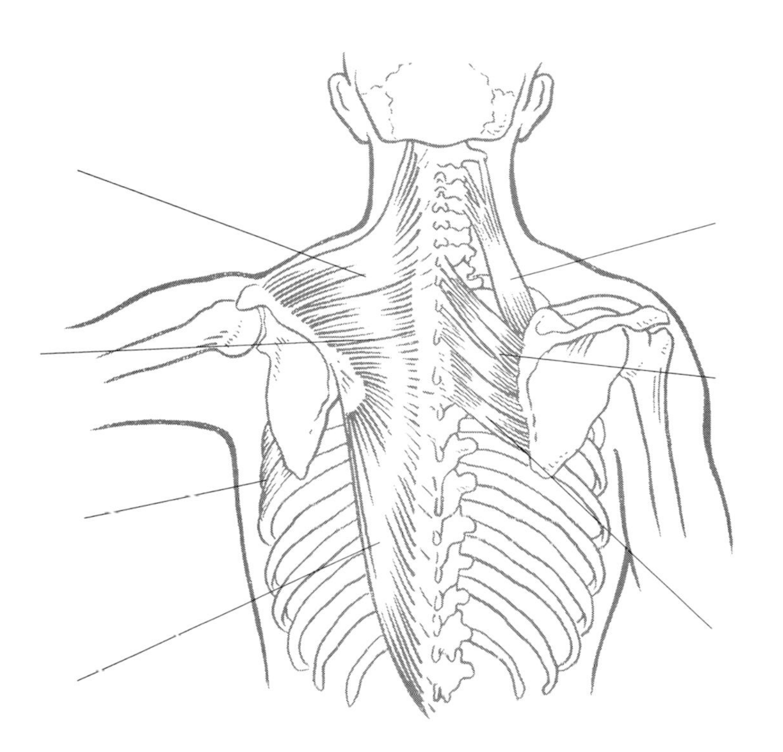

Show What You Know

I. Explain the dangers of working past the "burning" feeling that results when muscles are heavily exercised or in a state of fatigue.

II. Name the primary muscles or muscle groups that are utilized in the following situations.

a. leg extension at the knee

b. adduction at the shoulder

c. lateral flexion at the trunk

d. plantar flexion at the ankle

e. flexion at the elbow

f. adduction of the scapula

CHAPTER 3 Biomechanics and Applied Kinesiology

This chapter describes proper body alignment, how to identify the forces acting on the human body during movement, and how the bones, muscles and joints function to create movement. With this information you can analyze human movement and design exercises that are safe and effective for your client. After completing this section you will have a better understanding of:

- motive and resistive forces on the body
- physical laws affecting motion
- posture and muscle imbalance
- basic human motion terminology
- muscles and movement of the pelvis and lower extremity
- muscles acting at the hip and knee joint
- movement, function and implication of the upper-body muscles
- exercise analysis
- exercise design, instruction and correction

Vocabulary

- motive forces
- resistive forces
- lever arm
- torque
- inertia
- acceleration
- momentum
- center of gravity
- line of gravity
- neutral alignment
- scoliosis
- agonist
- antagonist
- co-contraction
- static action
- concentric action
- eccentric action

Reading Assignment

Read Chapter 3 of the *ACE Personal Trainer Manual,* paying special attention to the words listed in the box to the left. After you have read the chapter, define these words on a separate piece of paper.

Expand Your Knowledge

I. Analyze the following illustration of elbow extension and label the motive force (MF) and the resistive force (RF) during part 1 and part 2 of the movement.

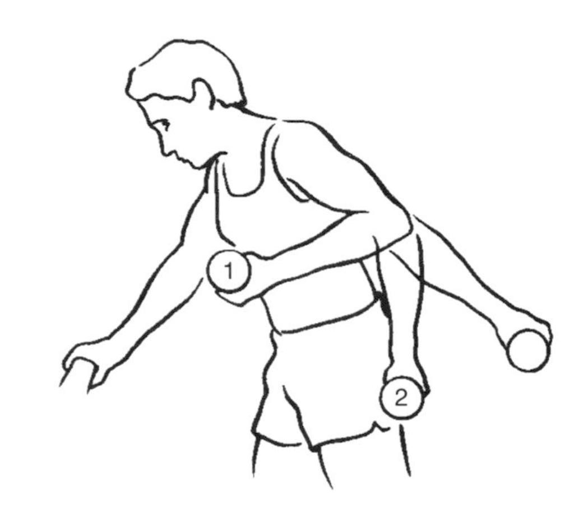

	Part 1	Part 2
Gravity	______	______
Biceps	______	______
Triceps	______	______
Dumbbell	______	______

II. Briefly describe how first and second class levers differ from a third-class lever.

____

____

____

____

____

III. Match the classical postural deviations on the left to the proper descriptions on the right.

a. ______ kyphosis-lordosis

b. ______ flat-back posture

c. ______ sway-back posture

d. ______ forward head posture

e. ______ scoliosis

1. a decrease in the normal inward curve of the low back, with the pelvis in posterior tilt
2. a long outward curve of the thoracic spine with an accentuated lumbar curve and a backward shift of the upper trunk
3. a lateral curve of the spine
4. an increase in the normal inward curve of the low back, increased flexion of the thoracic spine, rounded shoulders and a forward-tilted head
5. rounded shoulders, sunken chest and forward tilted head

IV. For a push-up performed on the ground, determine whether each of the following muscle groups are working as a prime mover (P), an antagonist (A), or a co-contractor (C) during the "up" phase.

a. ______ abdominal group

b. ______ anterior deltoid

c. ______ triceps

d. ______ pectoralis major

e. ______ hamstring group

f. ______ latissimus dorsi

V. Match the human motion terminology on the left to its definition on the right (from anatomical position). Indicate to the far left if the motion occurs in the sagittal (S), frontal (F), or transverse (T) planes, or if it is multiplanar (M).

	Plane	Match		Definition
1.	_____	_____	Depression	a. rotating the hand and wrist from the elbow to the palm up position (elbow flexed)
2.	_____	_____	Dorsiflexion	b. thumb movement that follows a semicircle toward the little finger
3.	_____	_____	Extension	c. moving the top of the foot toward the shin (ankle only)
4.	_____	_____	Supination	d. lifting the medial border of the foot (subtaler joint only)
5.	_____	_____	Adduction	e. motion toward the midline of the body (or part)
6.	_____	_____	Opposition	f. moving to an inferior position (scapula)
7.	_____	_____	Rotation	g. increasing the angle between two bones
8.	_____	_____	Inversion	h. medial (inward) or lateral (outward) turning about the vertical axis of the bone

VI. For each joint action given, list at least two muscles that are primary movers.

1. lateral flexion of the trunk ____________________

   ____

2. hip abduction ____________________

   ____

3. knee flexion ____________________

   ____

4. shoulder abduction ____________________

   ____

5. shoulder external rotation ____________________

   ____

6. plantarflexion and eversion ____________________

   ____

7. hip extension ____________________

   ____

8. scapular elevation ____________________

   ____

VII. A client, Tim, is performing a side deltoid raise (shoulder abduction) with the elbow flexed at 90 degrees while holding 20-pound weights in each hand. Describe three ways to increase the workload on the deltoid group.

____

____

____

____

____

Show What You Know

I. Arnold, a new client, is performing abdominal curls and you notice he has a forward head posture. Describe two ways to correct Arnold's position.

II. A client, Mary, shows you an exercise for the chest that she really likes. Mary stands with 15-pound weights in each hand, and, beginning in 90-degree shoulder abduction, performs chest flyes (horizontal shoulder adduction and abduction). Analyze this exercise to determine its effectiveness and recommend a modification to increase the workload on the chest muscle group.

CHAPTER **4** *Nutrition*

Vocabulary

- protein
- carbohydrate
- fat
- vitamin
- mineral
- essential nutrients
- nonessential nutrients
- Recommended Dietary Allowance (RDA)
- lipoproteins
- triglycerides
- carbohydrate loading
- glycemic index
- hydrogenation
- antioxidants
- athletic amenorrhea
- lactose intolerance

Getting Started

This chapter provides information on the basic nutrients and nutritional needs of physically active adults. After completing this section you will have a better understanding of:

- the six major classes of nutrients and their major functions
- the difference between essential and nonessential nutrients
- the food guide pyramid
- basic classifications of vegetarians
- the nutrient needs of the physically active
- diet and heart disease
- hydration and fluid replacement
- popular sports nutrition myths

Reading Assignment

Read Chapter 4 of the *ACE Personal Trainer Manual,* paying special attention to the words listed in the box to the left. After you have read the chapter, define these words on a separate piece of paper.

Expand Your Knowledge

I. Describe the difference between essential and nonessential nutrients.

II. List the six major classes of nutrients, their recommended intakes and the primary functions of each.

Major Classes of Nutrients	Recommended Intake	Primary Functions

III. Describe the difference between high-density lipoproteins and low-density lipoproteins.

IV. Label the food guide pyramid and list the recommended intakes for each group.

V. List the primary nutrients found in the Milk, Meat and Vegetable food groups.

a. Milk: ____________________

b. Meat: ____________________

c. Vegetable: ____________________

VI. Describe the difference between lacto-ovo-vegetarians and vegans.

____

____

____

VII. List the three guidelines for fluid replacement during exercise and physical activity.

1. ______________________________

____

2. ______________________________

____

3. ______________________________

____

VIII. Fill in the blanks.

a. We generally choose to eat certain foods because of their

______________________.

b. The most important nutrient for exercising muscles is

______________________.

c. The deposition of fat and cholesterol within the arteries is known as

______________________.

d. A good source of vitamins A, B_2, E, K and folate is

______________________.

e. The chemical process by which hydrogen atoms are added to unsaturated and polyunsaturated fats is ______________________.

Show What You Know

I. A client, Anna Bolick, has been a bodybuilder for two years. She approaches you with an advertisement for a protein supplement. Describe how you would discuss protein supplements with Anna.

II. A new client, Artie Tack, is mildly obese, deconditioned and eats whatever he wants. His doctor has just informed him that his blood cholesterol level is 245 mg/dl and that he is a heart attack waiting to happen. His doctor also told him he should exercise, but said nothing about diet. Describe how diet can contribute to the prevention of heart disease and recommend some simple fat substitutions for Artie.

Practice What You Know

Using the food guide pyramid, make recommendations for a three-day diet for a healthy 175-pound male who jogs 30 minutes every other day, and performs one set of 10 free-weight exercises two days per week.

CHAPTER 5 Health Screening

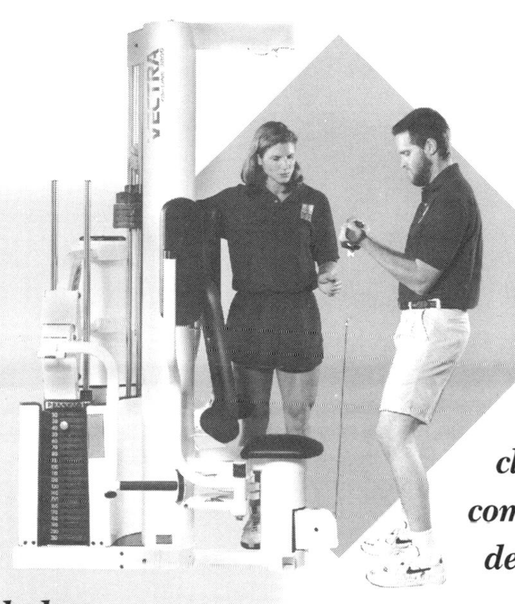

Getting Started

This chapter describes how to use your client's health history to create a safe and effective training program and identify situations that may necessitate medical clearance from a healthcare professional. After completing this section you will have a better understanding of:

- the components of a health history form
- conditions that require medical clearance
- guidelines for making professional referrals
- health conditions that affect physical activity
- the effects of medications on heart rate response
- the forms you can use to collect health history information and to gain medical approval to begin an exercise program

Vocabulary

- health history form
- atherosclerosis
- angina
- PAR-Q
- hypertension
- dyspnea
- hypertension
- hyperthyroid persons
- hernia
- beta blockers
- calcium channel blockers
- ACE inhibitors
- diuretics
- bronchodilators

Reading Assignment

Read Chapter 5 of the *ACE Personal Trainer Manual,* paying special attention to the words listed in the box to the left. After you have read the chapter, define these words on a separate piece of paper.

Expand Your Knowledge

I. List the seven components of a complete health history form.

1. ______
2. ______
3. ______
4. ______
5. ______
6. ______
7. ______

II. You are screening clients who are new to exercise. Place an (X) next to any health history response that warrants medical clearance.

a. ______ "I have been trying to become pregnant, but I'm not yet sure if I am."

b. ______ "Three months ago I had a stress fracture; it should be healed by now."

c. ______ "I am taking vitamin supplements."

d. ______ "I am taking birth control pills."

e. ______ "I'm a 56-year-old man who smokes, and my blood pressure is 142/92."

f. ______ "I am taking insulin."

g. ______ "I'm a completely healthy 42-year-old man."

III. List the professional requirements you must consider when referring clients to a healthcare professional.

______

______

______

______

______

IV. Fill in the chart to the right by placing a (↑) if the medication causes an increase, a (↓) if the medication causes a decrease, and a (←→) if the medication causes an insignificant effect. In some cases, more than one response may be appropriate.

Medication	Resting HR	Exercising HR	Maximal Exercising HR
Beta-adrenergic Blocking Agents			
Calcium Channel Blockers			
Caffeine			
Diuretics			
Antihypertensives			

V. Each of the following health conditions require preexercise medical clearance and special programming. Describe any potential risks that could result from physical activity.

a. hyperthyroid ______________________________

____

____

b. hernia ______________________________

____

____

c. diuretics ______________________________

____

____

d. chronic obstructive pulmonary disease (COPD) ______________________________

____

____

VI. Match the form on the right to the description on the left.

a. ______ is the minimal prerequisite to beginning a low- to moderate-intensity exercise program

b. ______ used to collect information about the client's past and present physical activities, dietary patterns and support systems

c. ______ used to obtain approval and recommendations from a licensed healthcare professional for clients who have health conditions that may be aggravated by vigorous exercise

d. ______ used to collect information about the client's past and present medical condition and to screen for any conditions that may be contraindicated

1. Physical Activity Readiness Questionnaire (PAR-Q)
2. Health History Form
3. Medical Release Form
4. Lifestyle Information Form

Show What You Know

I. Place the following steps and tools in the correct order by placing a number (1-5) in the space provided.

a. _____ physical screening

b. _____ assessment of any medications and their effect on exercise response

c. _____ assessment of risk factors and need for referral and/or physician clearance

d. _____ health history form and interview

e. _____ identification of lifestyle factors that may affect program design

II. A new client, Justin Case, is excited about starting an exercise program. Because Justin is a 41-year-old male, you ask him to get a full medical work-up before beginning an exercise routine. Justin becomes angry that he can't start working out, and states, "I've been healthy all my life. Why do I need to see a doctor?" Develop a script you can use to explain to Justin why he must get medical clearance before beginning an exercise program.

____

____

____

____

____

____

____

____

____

____

____

____

Practice What You Know

Use the forms from the ACE Personal Trainer Manual *to perform a trial health screening protocol. Ask a friend or relative to be your client for a practice session.*

CHAPTER

6 Testing and Evaluation

Vocabulary

- risk factors
- submaximal aerobic exercise test
- informed consent
- resting heart rate
- blood pressure
- palpation
- auscultation
- baroreceptors
- stroke volume
- systolic blood pressure
- diastolic blood pressure
- antecubital space
- maximal graded exercise test
- maximal oxygen uptake
- heart-rate reserve
- ratings of perceived exertion
- training heart rate
- physical working capacity
- fat-free mass
- adipose tissue
- residual volume
- bioelectric impedance
- body mass index (BMI)
- anthropometric assessments
- waist-to-hip circumference ratio (WTH)
- one-repetition max (1 RM)

Getting Started

This chapter describes a number of ways to test and evaluate your client's fitness level so you can make informed decisions about when, how and why to administer an exercise test. After completing this section you will have a better understanding of:

- the purposes of exercise testing
- the basic components of exercise assessment
- pretest and safety procedures
- methods for cardiorespiratory testing and evaluation
- ways to test and evaluate body composition
- methods for flexibility testing and evaluation
- ways to test and evaluate muscular strength and endurance

Reading Assignment

Read Chapter 6 of the *ACE Personal Trainer Manual,* paying special attention to the words listed in the box to the left. After you have read the chapter, define these words on a separate piece of paper.

Expand Your Knowledge

I. List the four components measured in a comprehensive exercise assessment.

1. ______________________________
2. ______________________________
3. ______________________________
4. ______________________________

II. Using the sample exercise history and attitude questionnaire (Figure 6.1), list several responses that indicate to you that the assessment process may be counterproductive.

____

____

____

____

____

____

____

____

III. Fill in the blanks.

a. The average resting heart rate is _______ bpm for men and _______ bpm for women.

b. A chronically __________________________ resting heart rate in a vigorous exerciser is a sign of overtraining.

c. During a submaximal exercise test, do not allow the exercising heart rate to exceed _______ percent of heart-rate reserve or maximal oxygen uptake.

d. To convert a 10-repetition-max weightload to a 1-repetition-max estimation, divide the weight load by _______ .

e. During a push-up test, the client is allowed to rest in the _______ position only.

IV. Explain at least one reason for performing each of the following pretest and safety procedures.

a. written consent

b. written emergency procedures

c. cardiovascular risk assessment

V. Indicate the proper order for each step in the blood pressure measurement procedure.

a. ______ Support the arm of the client on either the arm of a chair or your own arm.

b. ______ Determine the systolic blood pressure by listening for the first perception of sound.

c. ______ Release the pressure at the rate of about 2 mmHg per second.

d. ______ Seat the client with both feet on the floor for two minutes.

e. ______ Determine the diastolic pressure by noting when the sound ceases to be heard or becomes absent.

f. ______ Use the other side of the body to duplicate the measurement.

g. ______ Wrap the cuff smoothly and firmly around the client's arm.

h. ______ Place the stethoscope over the brachial artery.

i. ______ Rapidly inflate the cuff to 20 to 30 mmHg above the point where the pulse can no longer be felt at the wrist.

VI. Describe the major differences between the following pairs of words or phrases.

a. absolute maximal oxygen uptake and relative maximal oxygen uptake

b. upper-body obesity and lower-body obesity

c. muscular strength and muscular endurance

d. lower-weight/high-repetition muscular endurance test and higher-weight/low-repetition muscular endurance test

VII. List three guidelines that ensure the client's heart rate does not exceed 150 to 155 beats per minute during the Ross Submaximal Treadmill Test.

1. ____________________

2. ____________________

3. ____________________

VIII. Using formulas found in Chapter 6, calculate the results of each of the following examples of cardiorespiratory exercise assessments and determine the fitness category.

a. McArdle Step Test: 34-year-old male, 42 beats per 15 seconds
Determine estimated maximal VO_2 and fitness category:

b. McArdle Step Test: 44-year-old female, 41 beats per 15 seconds
Determine estimated maximal VO_2 and fitness category:

c. The Rockport Fitness Walking Test (1-mile Walk): 45-year-old female, 24 beats per 10 seconds, 14:37 minute mile walk time, 201 pounds
Determine estimated maximal VO_2 and fitness category:

d. YMCA Submaximal Step Test: 51-year-old male, 128 beats per minute
Determine fitness category:

IX. Explain the procedures for locating the following skinfold-measurement sites.

a. chest ______

______

b. abdomen ______

______

c. triceps ______

______

d. suprailium ______

______

X. List one advantage and one disadvantage for the following exercise assessment tests.

a. bench-press test ______

______

______

______

b. isometric strength testing ______

______

______

______

______

______

______

______

continued on next page

c. trunk flexion flexibility test

d. hydrostatic weighing

XI. Using formulas found in Chapter 6, calculate the results and determine the fitness category for the following examples of body-composition testing and evaluation.

a. Body mass index: 32-year-old female, 5'4", 130 pounds
Determine BMI and fitness category:

b. Skinfold measurements (Jackson and Pollock): 38-year-old male,
chest: 11 mm, abdomen: 23 mm, and thigh: 13 mm
Determine body-fat percentage and fitness category:

c. Estimated body fat from circumference measurements: 52-year-old female
5'7½", abdomen: 32 inches, hips: 39½ inches
Determine body-fat percentage and fitness category:

d. Estimated body-fat distribution: Using the information in the last question, determine waist-to-hip ratio and fitness category:

XII. Describe the implications of the following flexibility testing and evaluation results.

a. Shoulder adductor flexibility test: Arms do not lie flat.

b. Trunk flexion test: 28-year-old female, 16 inches with a trunk flexion evaluation of "Poor."

c. Shoulder multi-rotational flexibility test: Fingertips are not touching but are less than 2 inches apart.

d. Hip flexor flexibility test: Right leg lifts up off table as left leg reaches 80 degrees.

XIII. Identify the muscular strength and endurance test you would use in the following situations.

a. upper-body strength and endurance

____

b. abdominal strength and endurance

____

c. leg strength

____

Show What You Know

I. List five purposes for fitness testing and evaluation.

1. ______________________________

____

2. ______________________________

____

3. ______________________________

____

4. ______________________________

____

5. ______________________________

____

II. A new client, Addie Poze, currently weighs 176 pounds at 28 percent body fat. She would like to reduce her body fat to between 22 percent to 24 percent. Determine Addie's desired body weight.

III. A hardworking client, Max X. Ershun, wants you to evaluate his strength. There aren't enough weights available for Max to do a 1-repetition maximum. Max weighs 165 pounds and is 27 years old. He can bench press 220 pounds for 10 repetitions. Calculate Max's upper-body strength and identify his fitness classification.

CHAPTER

7 Cardiorespiratory Fitness and Exercise

Getting Started

This chapter describes different training methods and cardiorespiratory activities that can be used to develop an exercise program that meets the needs of your client. After completing this section you will have a better understanding of:

- cardiovascular health benefits and adaptive physiological responses
- components of cardiorespiratory exercise programming
- types of training methods
- methods of monitoring and measuring cardiorespiratory intensity
- guidelines for programming various activities
- special considerations and safety during cardiorespiratory programming

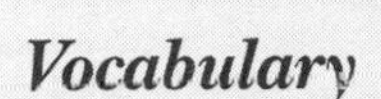

Vocabulary

- peripheral vascular resistance
- cardiorespiratory endurance
- functional capacity
- frequency
- duration
- intensity
- maximum heart rate
- maximal oxygen consumption
- heart rate reserve
- Karvonen Formula
- MET
- rating of perceived exertion (RPE)
- talk test
- continuous training
- interval training
- Fartlek training
- aerobic cross training
- age-predicted heart rate

Reading Assignment

Read Chapter 7 of the *ACE Personal Trainer Manual,* paying special attention to the words listed in the box to the left. After you have read the chapter, define these words on a separate sheet of paper.

Expand Your Knowledge

I. Art Turee, a new client, is interested in the cardiovascular benefits and physiological changes he can expect from his new fitness program. List five cardiovascular health benefits and five adaptive physiological responses.

Cardiovascular health benefits:

a. ____________________

b. ____________________

c. ____________________

d. ____________________

e. ____________________

Adaptive physiologic responses:

a. ____________________

b. ____________________

c. ____________________

d. ____________________

e. ____________________

II. Place a (WU) next to the rationale most closely associated with a warm-up; place a (CD) next to the rationale most closely associated with a cool-down.

a. ______ prevents metabolic problems during exercise

b. ______ prevents premature onset of blood lactic acid accumulation

c. ______ prevents muscle spasms or cramping

d. ______ prevents musculoskeletal injury as a result of stretching

e. ______ prevents blood pooling and risk of fainting

f. ______ reduces the risk of post-exercise disturbances in cardiac rhythm

III. Circle the one response that best fits the specific criteria for improving cardiorespiratory fitness.

Case #1: Jim is 42 years old, apparently healthy and a beginning exerciser. His goal is to lose 20 pounds in 12 months.

a. jogging, 3 times/week, 45 minutes, 80% VO_2 max

b. walking, 3 times/week, 45 minutes, 70% VO_2 max

c. jogging, 4 times/week, 15 minutes, 70% VO_2 max

d. walking, 4 times/week, 15 minutes, 80% VO_2 max

Case #2: Carrie is 29 years old, apparently healthy and an experienced exerciser. Her goal is to beat her husband in a 10K race in four months.

a. jogging, 3 times/week, 45 minutes, 80% VO_2 max

b. walking, 3 times/week, 45 minutes, 70% VO_2 max

c. jogging, 4 times/week, 15 minutes, 70% VO_2 max

d. walking, 4 times/week, 15 minutes, 80% VO_2 max

IV. Your client, Joseph King, has an 11 METS functional aerobic capacity and will be exercising at an intensity of 60 percent to 70 percent of his functional capacity. What is his exercise intensity range in METS? Using Table 7.8 (page 219) of the ACE Personal Trainer Manual, *list the mean MET value for the activities listed and place a (Yes) for activities within Joe's intensity range and a (No) for activities outside Joe's range.*

Exercise intensity range (METS):____________________

MET value	within range?	
______	______	a. cycling (10 mph)
______	______	b. rope jumping (60-80 skips/min)
______	______	c. table tennis
______	______	d. running (12 minute/mile)
______	______	e. climbing hills
______	______	f. boxing (sparring)

V. Compare target heart-rate ranges using intensity by percentage of maximum heart rate and intensity by the Karvonen Formula.

Use the following statistics:
Age: 30
Resting heart rate: 80
Desired intensity: 60-70%

a. Intensity range by percent maximum heart rate (in bpm):

____

b. Intensity range by Karvonen Formula (in bpm):

____

c. How are they different or the same?

____

____

VI. Fill in the blanks.

a. When using the new Borg scale, the average exerciser should be between the numbers ______ and ______.

b. Using the old Borg scale, a rating of 12 would indicate a heart rate of ______ bpm.

VII. Gabbie, your new client, is a beginning exerciser. Describe how you would explain the talk-test method to her.

____

____

____

____

VIII. Match up the descriptions to one of the following three conditioning stages:
IN = Initial
IM = Improvement
MA = Maintenance

a. _____ the rate of progression is fast

b. _____ intensity may be adjusted at lower than previous levels

c. _____ intensity adjustment is conservative

d. _____ there is no rate of progression

e. _____ the rate of progression is slow

f. _______intensity may be adjusted at higher than previous levels

IX. Explain how the following factors may influence the rate of increase in aerobic capacity.

a. initial level of fitness: ____

____

b. age: ____

____

____

c. duration of training: ____

____

____

____

X. Match the descriptions on the right to one of the five training methods on the left.

CON = continuous training

INT = interval training

FAR = Fartlek training

CIR = circuit training

AC = aerobic composite

a. ______ repeated periods of exercise interspersed with periods of relatively light exercise

b. ______ a combination of all the training methods

c. ______ cycles of work/rest periods that are not systematically or accurately measured

d. ______ a series of stations with brief periods in between

e. ______ a stage of exercise that is maintained at 50 percent and 85 percent of functional capacity

XI. List five reasons to temporarily defer exercise.

1. ______________________________

____

2. ______________________________

____

3. ______________________________

____

4. ______________________________

____

5. ______________________________

____

XII. Circle the option that makes the following statements more correct.

a. Beta-blocking and calcium-channel blocking drugs (**increase/decrease**) the heart-rate response to exercise.

b. Seat adjustment for a stationary cycle is with a (**slightly bent/straight**) leg in the down position.

c. Relatively experienced swimmers generate a heart-rate response that is (**lower/higher**) for any effort compared with that of cyclists and runners.

d. Healthy individuals (**are/are not**) greatly effected by an increase in CO_2 blood levels of 10 percent to 15 percent during moderate exercise.

e. After a full meal, an exerciser should (**wait at least 90 minutes/drink plenty of fluids/not worry about it**) before beginning their workout.

f. Tennis, racquetball and handball are largely (**aerobic/anaerobic**) activities for the beginning exerciser.

g. Aerobic dance exercisers generate a heart-rate response that is (**lower/higher**) for any effort compared with that of cyclists and runners.

Show What You Know

I. Describe how to locate the four pulse sites and the steps in heart-rate monitoring to a new client.

II. Case Study: Emma Rhee, an experienced exerciser, is bored with her existing cardiovascular workout and has hired you to help her add variety. Create a 16-week exercise plan that outlines Emma's mode, frequency, intensity, duration and method. Her workout will be updated after eight weeks. (Age: 50; Resting heart rate: 70; Weight: 160 pounds; Percent body fat: 25)

	Current	Weeks 1-8	Weeks 9-16
Mode	swimming and cycling		
Intensity	does not monitor		
Frequency	2-4x/week		
Duration	30 minutes		
Method	continuous training		

Practice What You Know

Monitor your heart rate while exercising and compare it to the perceived exertion scale. Then practice monitoring heart rate on a friend or client.

CHAPTER 8 Muscular Strength and Endurance

Getting Started

This chapter describes the benefits of strength training and methods of helping your clients gain the results they want by incorporating various types of training equipment, guidelines and program considerations. After completing this section you will have a better understanding of:

- the benefits of strength training
- biomechanical and physiological factors that affect strength
- the relationship between muscular strength and endurance
- advantages and disadvantages of strength-training equipment
- the guidelines and considerations for effective strength training

Vocabulary

- strength training
- physical capacity
- metabolic function
- isometric contraction
- concentric contraction
- eccentric contraction
- prime mover
- motor units
- muscle fatigue
- muscle soreness
- muscle strength
- muscle endurance
- circuit training
- spotting
- anabolic steroids
- strength plateaus
- periodization

Reading Assignment

Read Chapter 8 of the *ACE Personal Trainer Manual,* paying special attention to the words listed in the box to the left. After you have read the chapter, define these words on a separate piece of paper.

Expand Your Knowledge

I. List at least one advantage and one disadvantage of each of the following types of strength-training equipment.

a. Isometric equipment

advantage ______________________

____

disadvantage ______________________

____

b. Isokinetic equipment

advantage ______________________

____

disadvantage ______________________

____

c. Dynamic constant resistance equipment

advantage ______________________

____

disadvantage ______________________

____

d. Dynamic variable resistance equipment

advantage ______________________

____

disadvantage ______________________

____

II. Match the training strategies on the right with the training examples on the left.

1._____ a partner actually helps the client perform two or three post-fatigue repetitions

2._____ a set of triceps extensions is immediately followed by a set of triceps dips

3._____ completing a set of leg curls with 55 pounds, immediately followed by a set with a 45-pound weightload

4._____ lowering weights that are too heavy to lift

5._____ using different exercises that target the same muscle group to further strength development

6._____ taking 10 seconds for each lifting movement and four seconds for the lowering movement

7._____ one month of 12 to 16 reps, then one month of 8 to 12 reps, followed by one month of 4 to 8 reps

8._____ decreasing or increasing the number of workouts in a week

a. Breakdown training

b. Slow training

c. Assisted training

d. Negative training

e. Periodization

f. Training sets

g. Training exercises

h. Training frequency

III. Describe how strength training benefits the following four areas.

a. physical capacity ____

____

b. physical appearance ______________________________________

____

c. metabolic functions ______________________________________

____

d. injury risk ____

____

IV. Barbara Bell bench presses a maximum of 120 pounds. Calculate her 12-repetition maximum weight.

V. Circle the correct response or responses for each of the following statements.

1. Men and women can increase their muscular strength during which of the following age groups:

   a. 10 to 20
   b. 20 to 30
   c. 30 to 40
   d. 40 to 50
   e. 50 to 60
   f. 70+

2. Which factors increase a person's physical capacity to generate effective force output:

   a. percentage of fast twitch fibers
   b. shorter limbs
   c. tendon insertion closer to joint action
   d. gender

VI. Describe the differences between the major fiber types.

____

____

____

____

Show What You Know

I. A client, Anita Lift, can perform a maximum leg extension of 100 pounds. Calculate the amount of weight she should use for the following number of repetitions: (a) 6 repetitions (b) 8 repetitions (c) 10 repetitions (d) 12 repetitions

II. Explain why muscular strength training is recommended every other day rather than daily.

Practice What You Know

Take a basic workout that you, a client or a friend has used regularly and create a new workout by implementing two or three of the training strategies discussed in this chapter.

CHAPTER 9 # Strength Training Program Design

Vocabulary

- plyometrics
- intensity
- active recovery
- fast-twitch fibers
- slow-twitch fibers
- one-repetition max (1RM)
- ATP-CP energy systems
- lactic acid system
- cross training
- osteoporosis
- sets
- resistance
- repetitions
- periodization

Getting Started

This chapter describes a number of ways to create and modify a strength-training program that will meet the psychological and physical needs of your client. After completing this section you will have a better understanding of:

- basic questions to use to gather important programming information
- four basic program designs
- how to determine proper intensity
- how to plan recovery phases
- indicators for changing a strength program
- the practical applications of strength design
- the basics of periodization
- record-keeping basics
- examples of exercises for major muscle groups with performance recommendations and spotting tips

Reading Assignment

Read Chapter 9 of the *ACE Personal Trainer Manual,* paying special attention to the words listed in the box to the left. After you have read the chapter, define these words on a separate piece of paper.

Expand Your Knowledge

I. List some basic questions you can ask your clients that will help you understand their programming needs.

____

____

____

____

____

____

____

II. Determine whether the following program descriptions are examples of a health and fitness gain (H), functional training (F), bodybuilding (B), or competitive athlete (C) program design scenario.

a. ______ uses high intensity volume stress; three to six sets, 10 to 15 repetitions per exercise

b. ______ integrates balance and intrinsic muscular stability; closed-chain exercises

c. ______ plyometrics and skill practice; developing base strength

d. ______ at least 10 exercises, one set, eight to 12 repetitions, twice per week

III. A moderately motivated client, Anita Napp, is performing pull-ups. Create a list of possible exercises Anita could perform as active recovery.

____

____

____

____

____

____

IV. Fill in the blanks.

a. The average time it takes to establish a client's strength foundation is

______________________.

b. Load x repetitions x sets = ____________________.

c. For the average client, the recommended movement speed is

______________ per repetition.

d. A safe starting resistance for most clients is one that allows completion of

at least ______________________________ repetitions.

V. Using the information provided in the case study in Chapter 9 of the ACE Personal Trainer Manual, *explain the rationale behind the differences in programming for John and Janet in the following areas.*

a. load: ____

____

____

b. rest/recovery: ____

____

____

c. number of exercises: ____

____

____

____

____

VI. Match the step in the periodization model on the left to the example on the right.

1. set the goal
2. determine how to achieve the goal
3. identify training phases
4. plan volume and intensity
5. evaluate the program

a. ______ choose activities the client enjoys

b. ______ after active recovery, start a new meso-cycle at a slightly lower intensity than the previous cycle

c. ______ recognize goal achievement

d. ______ develop a three- to 10-day short-term plan (microcycle)

e. ______ establish baseline levels of fitness

f. ______ apply frequency, intensity and duration to each fitness component in the general preparation phase and goal phase

g. ______ change at least every three to four weeks, possibly within a three- to 10-day micro-cycle

VII. List items to be included in accurate lifting records.

____

____

____

VIII. Complete the following table.

Loading	Outcome	%1RM	Rep Range	# of sets	Rest
Light					
Moderate					
Heavy					

IX. List the three general guidelines for change when modifying strength-training programs to create overload.

1. ______________________________

____

2. ______________________________

____

3. ______________________________

____

Show What You Know

I. A new client, Rita Lott, has no experience strength training. However, she wants to strength train six days per week because she read that her favorite talk show host trains that often. Develop a script to explain to Rita the benefits of beginning with a strength-training program that she will participate in twice a week.

II. Describe the spotting recommendations for the following exercises.

a. push-up

b. pull-up/chin-up

c. free-weight medial deltoid

d. forward lunge

Practice What You Know

Use the periodization model in Chapter 9 of the ACE Personal Trainer Manual *to develop an eight-week starter program.*

CHAPTER **10** *Flexibility*

Getting Started

This chapter describes the science and research behind flexibility training methods that will help your clients attain their fitness goals and decrease their risk of injury. After completing this section you will have a better understanding of:

- flexibility basics
- the mechanics of stretching
- the sensory organs responsible for the stretch reflex
- the categories and types of stretching
- factors affecting flexibility
- the principles of stretching
- flexibility exercises for major muscle groups

Vocabulary

- range of motion (ROM)
- static flexibility
- dynamic flexibility
- connective tissue
- elastic stretch
- plastic stretch
- myostatic stretch reflex
- golgi tendon organs (GTO)
- neural receptors
- muscle spindles
- autogenic inhibition
- static stretching
- ballistic stretching
- proprioceptive neuro-muscular facilitation (PNF)
- hypokinesis

Reading Assignment

Read Chapter 10 of the *ACE Personal Trainer Manual,* paying special attention to the words listed in the box to the left. After you have read the chapter, define these words on a separate piece of paper.

Expand Your Knowledge

I. List at least five benefits of a flexibility-training program.

1. ____________________

____

2. ____________________

____

3. ____________________

____

4. ____________________

____

5. ____________________

____

II. Place the following steps in the myotatic stretch reflex in the proper order.

a. _____ the spinal cord sends an order to create a sudden protective muscular contraction

b. _____ the velocity of the muscle length change activates the muscle spindle

c. _____ the muscle spindle ceases to fire as muscle shortening begins

d. _____ the muscle spindle sends a signal to the spinal cord

e. _____ the muscle fiber and the muscle spindle stretch

III. Explain the major difference between the terms or phrases in the following pairs.

a. passive stretching and active stretching ______________________________

____

____

____

b. static flexibility and dynamic flexibility ______________________________

____

____

c. elastic stretch and plastic stretch ______________________________

____

____

d. stretching before exercise and stretching after exercise ________________

____

____

____

____

e. low-force, long-duration stretching, and high-force, short-duration stretching

____

____

____

IV. Describe the three basic stretching methods.

a. static ____

____

b. ballistic ____

____

c. PNF ____

____

____

____

V. Place a (WU) next to the statement that best describes a warm-up and (CD) next to the statement that best describes a cool-down.

a. _____ the goal of the stretching is muscle preparation

b. _____ the goal of the stretching is permanent muscle elongation

c. _____ body temperature is high

d. _____ body temperature is cold

e. _____ active stretching

f. _____ static stretching

VI. Describe what effect the following factors have on flexibility.

a. age

b. gender

c. body type

d. warm-up

VII. List the factors that limit joint mobility.

Show What You Know

I. Describe the body positioning necessary to stretch the following muscle groups from a standing position.

a. gastrocnemius ______________________________

____

b. soleus ______________________________

____

c. quadriceps ______________________________

____

d. hamstrings ______________________________

____

e. anterior shoulder ______________________________

____

II. Describe how you would coach a client performing a hamstring stretch for each of the following stretching methods.

a. static ______________________________

b. ballistic ______________________________

c. PNF ______________________________

____

CHAPTER **11** *Programming for the Healthy Adult*

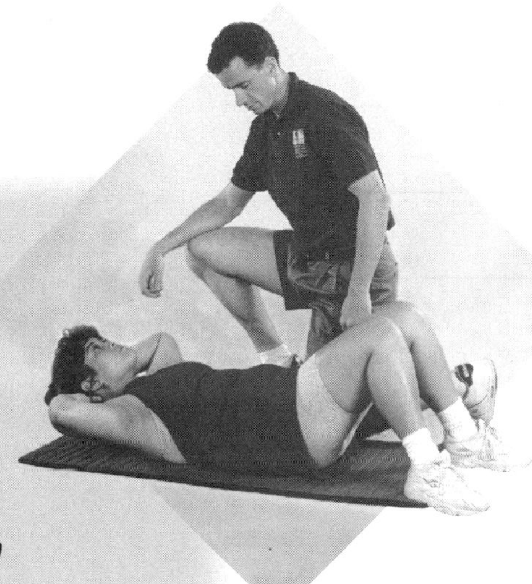

Getting Started

This chapter describes how to combine the basic components of exercise physiology to provide comprehensive exercise programs for your clients. After completing this section you will have a better understanding of:

- the basics of program design
- programming for physical fitness compared to health and disease prevention
- the traits of a good exercise consultant
- the guidelines for rate of progression and retesting
- practical application through case study

Vocabulary

- exercise lite
- cardiorespiratory endurance
- sedentary lifestyle
- medical/health screening
- physical fitness screening
- aerobic exercise mode
- heart-rate reserve
- flexibility
- body composition
- rating of perceived exertion
- contracting
- conditioning stages

Reading Assignment

Read Chapter 11 of the *ACE Personal Trainer Manual,* paying special attention to the words listed in the box to the left. After you have read the chapter, define these words on a separate piece of paper.

Expand Your Knowledge

I. List the four primary steps in designing a comprehensive exercise program.

1. ______________________________
2. ______________________________
3. ______________________________
4. ______________________________

____

II. Describe the rationale behind the ACSM's "exercise lite" guidelines.

____

____

____

____

____

____

____

____

III. Place the following steps in the program design process in the proper order.

a. _____ present your client with a list of aerobic activities

b. _____ share normative information on each fitness test with your client

c. _____ gain a complete picture of your client's medical and health status

d. _____ emphasize the importance of elevating the body temperature though slow aerobic movement

e. _____ review the principles of flexibility

f. _____ administer a fitness test

g. _____ identify clients that need more extensive medical clearance

IV. Match the traits of a good exercise consultant on the left with the descriptions on the right.

1. empathy
2. respect
3. warmth
4. genuineness
5. concreteness
6. self-disclosure
7. potency and self-actualization

a. _____ sharing a story of your own failure to lose weight

b. _____ the opposite of "do as I say, not as I do"

c. _____ seeing things through your client's eyes

d. _____ showing concern and being available

e. _____ conveying a secureness in your self

f. _____ appreciating the worth of your client

g. _____ solidifying essential ideas and elements

V. Describe the important characteristics of each of the following progression stages.

a. initial conditioning stage ______

______

______

b. improvement conditioning stage ______

______

______

c. maintenance conditioning stage ______

______

______

VI. Review the case histories found in Chapter 11 of the ACE Personal Trainer Manual. *Describe the rationale behind the following programming decisions.*

Case Study #1: A middle-aged American female

Start the client out with a 10-minute warm-up, followed by 15 minutes of cardiovascular activity at 50 percent to 60 percent of heart-rate reserve, three days per week.

______

______

______

______

______

______

______

continued on next page

Case Study #2: A 30-year-old male

Choose to bicycle or row over walking or running.

____

____

____

____

____

____

____

Case Study #3: An elderly male

Start the client out with a 10-minute warm-up, followed by 15 minutes of walking at 40 percent to 50 percent of heart-rate reserve, three days per week.

____

____

____

VII. Fill in the blanks.

a. Each year the number of Americans who suffer from a heart attack during or after exercise is ____________________.

b. The primary reason people give for not beginning an exercise program is ____________________.

c. According to the ACSM's exercise lite guidelines, the general population is urged "to accumulate ________ minutes or more of moderate-intensity physical activity over the course of most days."

d. Maintaining physical fitness is possible even when the training volume is decreased by ____________.

Show What You Know

I. Explain why walking is a great choice for the beginning exerciser.

II. Develop a fitness program given the following information.

Client: 38-year-old male
Weight: 170 pounds
Smoking status: never smoked
Personal history of disease: negative
Dietary habits: follows food pyramid
Personal fitness goals: maintenance and cross training
Fitness rating: high-average, except flexibility, which is poor

Height: 72 inches
Desired Weight: 170 pounds
Exercise habits: Swims 3x/week 35 minutes, 60 to 75% HRR; strength trains 2x/week, 1 set - 8 to 12 repetitions, 12 exercises

CHAPTER

12 Special Populations and Health Concerns

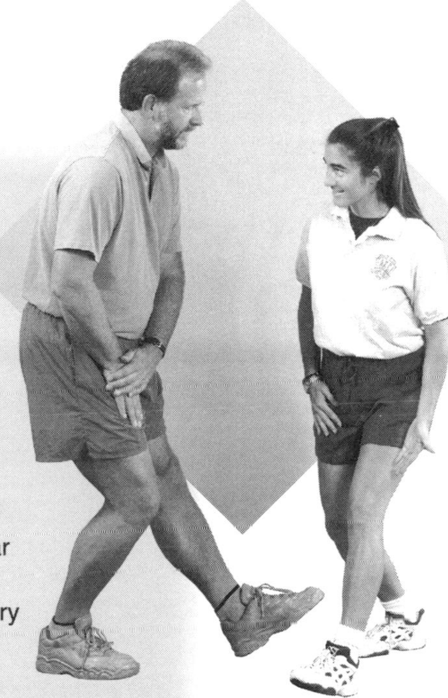

Getting Started

This chapter describes a variety of client health concerns you are likely to encounter, and modifications to basic exercises that can emphasize the safety and effectiveness of the workout. After completing this section you will have a better understanding of:

- exercise guidelines for cardiovascular health disorders and diabetes
- respiratory disorders and recommendations for exercise
- exercising with cancer
- the effects of exercise on osteoporosis and arthritis
- exercise guidelines for lower-back pain
- exercise and weight management
- recommendations for exercising for older adults and children
- exercise and pregnancy

Vocabulary

- cardiovascular disease
- coronary artery disease
- ischemia
- arrythmias
- hypertension
- valsalva maneuver
- cerebrovascular accidents (CVA)
- transient ischemic attacks (TIA)
- thrombosis
- vasoconstriction
- hyperglycemia
- hypoglycemia
- emphysema
- chronic obstructive pulmonary disease (COPD)
- osteoporosis
- postmenopausal
- herniated disc
- spondylolithesis
- basal metabolic rate
- hyperlipidemia
- resting metabolic rate

Reading Assignment

Read Chapter 12 of the *ACE Personal Trainer Manual,* paying special attention to the words listed in the box to the left. After you have read the chapter, define these words on a separate piece of paper.

Expand Your Knowledge

I. Consider the effect of aging on the following physiological areas. Place an (I) next to the areas that tend to increase during the aging process, a (D) for those areas that decrease and an (NC) for those areas that do not change during the aging process.

a. _____ maximal heart rate

b. _____ submaximal exercising blood pressure

c. _____ maximum oxygen uptake

d. _____ basal metabolic rate

e. _____ coordination

II. Which of the following three types of exercise programs would you recommend for an obese client who wants to lose weight? Explain why you would recommend that program.

1. aerobic endurance training only
2. strength training only
3. a combination of aerobic endurance and strength training

____

____

____

____

____

____

III. Match the health concern on the left to the exercise recommendation on the right. In some cases, the exercise recommendation may apply to more than one health concern.

1. low-back pain
2. arthritis
3. osteoporosis
4. asthma
5. bronchitis and emphysema

a. _____ extend the warm-up and cool-down periods

b. _____ initially, avoid upper-body exercises

c. _____ avoid extreme environmental conditions (high temperature or low temperature)

d. _____ avoid head-forward positions in which the chin is tilted up

e. _____ use isometric strengthening exercises

IV. List the types of movements that clients diagnosed with lower-back pain should avoid.

____

____

____

____

____

____

V. List the exercise guidelines for a low-risk client with cardiovascular artery disease.

a. intensity ______________________________

____

b. duration ______________________________

____

c. frequency ______________________________

____

VI. Match the health concern on the left to the exercise recommendation on the right. In some cases, the exercise recommendation may apply to more than one health concern.

1. hypertension
2. peripheral vascular disease (PVD)
3. diabetes

a. _____ exercise at the same time each day for better control

b. _____ avoid holding breath or straining during exercise (the valsalva maneuver)

c. _____ avoid exercising in cold air or water to reduce the risk of vasoconstriction

d. _____ give special attention to feet and foot care

e. _____ no heavy weight lifting; keep resistance low and repetitions high

f. _____ instruct your client to move slowly when getting up from the floor

VII. Explain the major difference between the terms or phrases in the following pairs.

a. bronchitis and emphysema ______________________________

____

____

____

b. osteoarthritis and rheumatoid arthritis ______________________________

____

____

____

continued on next page

c. insulin-dependent diabetes mellitus (IDDM) and non-insulin-dependent diabetes mellitus (NIDDM) ______________________________

d. cerebrovascular accidents (CVA) and myocardial infarction ________

VIII. List the types of activities clients with osteoporosis should avoid.

Show What You Know

I. Describe how you would gradually reduce the intensity, duration and frequency of a pregnant client's workout that consisted of high-impact aerobics three times per week and cycling outdoors 20 miles/day (75 minutes) two days per week.

a. first trimester ________________________________

____

b. second trimester ________________________________

____

____

c. third trimester ________________________________

____

II. You have taken on a new client, Ima Young, who is an 11-year-old girl. Her parents hired you because the physical education program at her school has been dropped. Describe the general recommendations you would make for Ima in the following areas.

a. mode ________________________________

____

b. intensity ________________________________

____

c. frequency ________________________________

____

d. duration ________________________________

____

e. strength training ________________________________

____

____

____

CHAPTER 13

Principles of Adherence and Motivation

Vocabulary

- adherence
- personal factors
- program factors
- environmental factors
- convenience
- motivation
- exercise expectations
- critical period
- leadership qualities
- professionalism
- goal setting
- prompts
- social support
- contract
- self-management
- lapses
- modeling

Getting Started

This chapter describes the factors that influence exercise adherence, and methods for keeping your clients involved in their exercise program. After completing this section you will have a better understanding of:

- the basics of exercise adherence
- factors influencing exercise adherence
- client motivation
- leadership qualities that affect exercise adherence
- methods for enhancing and maintaining motivation to exercise

Reading Assignment

Read Chapter 13 of the *ACE Personal Trainer Manual,* paying special attention to the words listed in the box to the left. After you have read the chapter, define these words on a separate piece of paper.

Expand Your Knowledge

I. When assessing a client's likelihood of maintaining an exercise program, determine whether the following conditions are indications of a personal factor (PER), a program factor (PRO) or an environmental factor (ENV).

a. ______ competing demands of family and work

b. ______ client's self-confidence in being able to engage in physical activity

c. ______ client's perception of support from friends and family

d. ______ friendliness of the workout facility

e. ______ support from friends and family

II. A client has just missed a week of exercising due to a family crisis. Describe the steps you would take to help the client maintain their exercise program.

____

____

____

____

III. Provide an example of a behavior a personal trainer can demonstrate for each of the following leadership qualities.

a. professionalism ______________________

b. dedication ______________________

c. sensitivity ______________________

d. recognizing signs of burnout ______________________

e. punctuality ______________________

IV. Fill in the blanks.

a. In a standard exercise program, the percentage of participants likely to drop out by the first six months is ____________________.

b. ____________________ is the most often-cited reason for discontinuing a vigorous exercise program.

c. It is estimated that ________ percent of the American population exercises at a level necessary to improve cardiovascular fitness.

d. The first three to six months of exercise, when many of the difficulties associated with maintaining a fitness regime normally occur, is called the initial ____________________.

V. When discussing client motivation and exercise adherence, what is meant by the term "blaming the victim"?

VI. List possible negative side effects that may accompany increased physical activity.

Show What You Know

I. You have acquired a new client, Joe Kammle, who needs to lose weight for medical reasons but is unwilling to stop smoking. After a month of working hard, Joe is beginning to lose interest in exercising. Describe the steps you can take to maintain Joe's healthy exercise behavior.

II. List some of the short term benefits of exercise and explain when it may be necessary to emphasize them.

Practice What You Know

Interview four to five active personal trainers to find out how they deal with burnout and how they help motivate clients.

CHAPTER 14 Communication and Teaching Techniques

Vocabulary

- helping relationship
- rapport stage
- investigation stage
- planning stage
- action stage
- empathy
- warmth
- genuineness
- attending behaviors
- modeling
- contracting
- feedback

This chapter describes various methods of establishing and maintaining a helping relationship with your clients that will enable them to successfully undergo positive lifestyle changes. After completing this section you will have a better understanding of:

- the stages of the personal trainer/client relationship
- nonverbal and verbal communication skills
- the SMART method of goal setting
- the pathways (visual, auditory and kinesthetic) clients use to gather information
- basic teaching techniques
- contracting as a means of behavioral reinforcement
- the three characteristics of effective feedback

Reading Assignment

Read Chapter 14 of the *ACE Personal Trainer Manual,* paying special attention to the words listed in the box to the left. After you have read the chapter, define these words on a separate piece of paper.

Expand Your Knowledge

I. Label the following events or steps according to whether they are more likely to occur during the Rapport stage (R), the Investigation stage (I), the Planning stage (P) or the Action stage (A).

a. _____ administering a health history questionnaire

b. _____ explanation, demonstration and execution

c. _____ communicating empathy, warmth and genuineness

d. _____ proposing possible alternatives to reaching the goal

II. Match the nonverbal behaviors on the left with the proper descriptions on the right.

a. _____ gestures	1. sensitively matching the posture and gesture of the other person
b. _____ eye contact	2. appropriate body movements that are relaxed rather than rigid
c. _____ positioning	3. pleasant surroundings that facilitate communication
d. _____ posture	4. intimate space, personal space, social distance or public distance
e. _____ environment	5. maintaining an open position with the legs and arms uncrossed
f. _____ mirroring	6. a relaxed focus that conveys your interest

III. Modify the following goals to more closely represent the SMART method of goal setting.

a. I want to maintain my current, comfortable weight throughout the holidays.

____

____

____

b. I want to lose 35 pounds in three months.

____

____

____

c. I want to improve my muscle tone, especially in my lower body.

____

____

____

IV. Place a (V) next to the trainer's visual strategies, an (A) next to the auditory strategies and a (K) next to the kinesthetic strategies.

a. _____ counting repetitions

b. _____ pressing the client's shoulders down during biceps curls

c. _____ showing the client the muscle group being worked

d. _____ touching the muscle group the client is working

e. _____ demonstrating a proper lift

f. _____ stating the muscle group the client is working

V. List the two components of a complete behavioral contract.

1. ____

2. ____

VI. Change the following closed-ended questions to open-ended questions.

a. Did you have a good workout today?

____

b. Have you been filling out your food diary?

____

c. Did you want to work out in the weight room or the cardio room today?

____

VII. List the three characteristics of effective feedback.

1. ______________________________

2. ______________________________

3. ______________________________

Show What You Know

I. You are training a new client, Max Energy, who expressed his dislike for cooling down after his morning running session. Using the Tell-Show-Do method of educating, create a lesson plan for teaching Max a proper cool down.

a. Tell

b. Show

c. Do

II. Upon attempting to teach Max Energy a proper cool-down, he displays resistance to learning.

a. List some of the nonverbal cues you are likely to observe from Max.

b. Create questions that you can use to discern why Max prefers not to cool down.

c. Create a summary you can use to conclude the session with Max.

Practice What You Know

Think of an experience you have had in a helping relationship, as either the helper or the client. Outline the events that occurred in the relationship and place them into the four stages of relationship building: Rapport, Investigation, Planning and Action.

CHAPTER

15 Musculoskeletal Injuries

Getting Started

This chapter describes how to develop programs for clients with pre-existing musculoskeletal injuries in order to minimize their risk of further injury. After completing this section you will have a better understanding of:

- basic tissue functions and the effects of injury on each type of tissue
- the signs and symptoms of inflammation
- the RICE method of treating acute musculoskeletal injuries
- exercises to avoid for clients with common pre-existing musculoskeletal injuries
- environmental impact on injuries

Vocabulary

- muscle tissue
- tendon tissue
- ligament tissue
- collagen tissue
- bone tissue
- muscle strain
- inflammation
- RICE
- heat cramps
- heat stroke
- heat exhaustion
- hypothermia

Reading Assignment

Read Chapter 15 of the *ACE Personal Trainer Manual,* paying special attention to the words listed in the box to the left. After you have read the chapter, define these words on a separate piece of paper.

Expand Your Knowledge

I. Label the following descriptions as either muscle tissue (M), tendon (T), bone (B) or ligament (L).

a. _____ connects bone to bone

b. _____ connects bone to muscle

c. _____ these injuries heal with scar tissue known as collagen tissue

d. _____ repairs itself with exactly the same type of tissue when injured

e. _____ does not contract to protect the area when injured

II. Describe the immediate care for victims of the following conditions.

a. heat-related illness ____

____

____

b. hypothermia ____

____

____

III. Match the pre-existing condition on the right with the preventative programming description on the left.

Preventative Programming Description	Musculoskeletal Injury
1. _____ strengthening the peroneal muscles	a. shoulder impingement syndrome
2. _____ decrease impact forces to lower legs and increase flexibility to Achilles tendon and posterior muscles of calf; decrease fallen arches and flat feet	b. dislocating shoulder
3. _____ minimize extreme shoulder abduction and external rotation	c. spinal injuries
4. _____ increase flexibility of the flexor group of the lower arm	d. carpal tunnel syndrome
5. _____ avoid overhead presses, lat pull downs and incline presses	e. ankle sprain
6. _____ avoid overhead presses, increasing abdominal strength and hamstring flexibility	f. runner's knee or jumper's knee
7. _____ eccentric strengthening in the legs	g. shin splints syndrome

IV. Describe the standard first-aid treatment of acute musculoskeletal injuries.

R ______________________________

I ______________________________

C ______________________________

E ______________________________

V. List the five signs or symptoms of inflammation.

1. ______________________________

2. ______________________________

3. ______________________________

4. ______________________________

5. ______________________________

Show What You Know

I. How would you modify the following activities to suit the needs of the client?

a. bench press for the client with carpel tunnel syndrome

b. jogging for the client with shin splint syndrome

c. running outside on an extremely hot and humid day

II. A client, Sue Reddy, complains of a pinpoint pain in the medial side of her lower leg. What should you recommend?

Practice What You Know

Write out a protocol for treating acute musculoskeletal injuries that you can use while training. Remember to check with your local governing associations for the most current standards for providing emergency treatment.

CHAPTER

16 Emergency Procedures

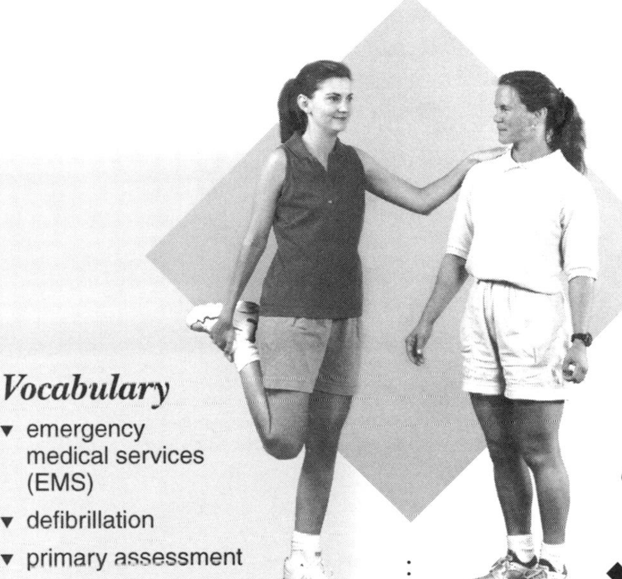

Getting Started

This chapter describes most of the common medical emergencies you might encounter as a personal trainer, and first aid procedures for responding to them. After completing this section you will have a better understanding of:

- various types of emergency equipment and emergency medical services
- the steps for primary and secondary assessment
- the ABCs of basic life support
- symptoms for common medical emergencies and injuries
- practices that may prevent medical emergencies
- blood-borne pathogens and how to avoid unnecessary exposure

Vocabulary

- emergency medical services (EMS)
- defibrillation
- primary assessment
- secondary assessment
- dyspnea
- asthma
- cyanosis
- exercise-induced asthma
- coronary artery disease (CAD)
- angina
- myocardial infarction
- syncope
- hypoglycemia
- diabetes mellitus
- acclimatization
- grand mal seizure
- postictal phase
- abrasion
- incision
- laceration
- puncture
- avulsion
- sprain

Reading Assignment

Read Chapter 16 of the *ACE Personal Trainer Manual,* paying special attention to the words listed in the box to the left. After you have read the chapter, define these words on a separate piece of paper.

Expand Your Knowledge

I. List five items that should always be stocked in a first-aid kit.

1. ______
2. ______
3. ______
4. ______
5. ______

II. List six possible steps during a secondary assessment process.

1. ______
2. ______
3. ______
4. ______
5. ______
6. ______

III. List and briefly describe the four phases of a typical grand mal seizure.

1. ______
______
2. ______
______
3. ______
______
4. ______
______

IV. Describe the major difference between the following pairs of words or phrases.

a. emergency medical technicians (EMTs) and paramedics

b. primary assessment and secondary assessment

c. angina and myocardial infarction

d. a simple (closed) fracture and a compound (open) fracture

continued on next page

e. sprains and strains

____

____

____

V. Match the common medical emergencies and injuries on the left to the symptoms on the right.

1. asthma
2. hypoglycemia
3. spinal cord injury
4. myocardial infarction
5. avulsion
6. laceration
7. heat exhaustion

a. _____ wheezing or whistling sound when breathing, flared nostrils and inability to speak

b. _____ obvious numbness, weakness or tingling of an extremity

c. _____ fatigue, headache, trembling, excessive sweating, slurred speech, poor coordination and elevated blood pressure

d. _____ cut or irregular tear in the soft tissues; bleeding may be brisk

e. _____ fatigue, severe headache, vomiting, nausea, light-headedness, tachycardia and hypotension

f. _____ nausea and vomiting, excessive sweating, difficult breathing, light-headedness, and pain or pressure sensation over the chest, shoulder, neck and/or back

g. _____ a forcible tearing away of the tissue from the body

VI. List the complete steps in a primary assessment process.

1. ______________________________

____

2. ______________________________

____

3. ______________________________

____

4. ______________________________

____

____

5. ______________________________

VII. List the ABCs of basic life support and explain the advantages of the ABC sequence as compared to the CBA sequence.

A = ______________________

B = ______________________

C = ______________________

____

____

____

____

____

Show What You Know

I. A prospective client approaches you to begin personal training. She is a diabetic and has come to you after her doctor suggested she start exercising. She is intimidated by her doctor and was afraid to ask him about the specific details of how and when she should exercise. Describe some of the particular guidelines she should consider when beginning to exercise so she can approach her doctor for more information.

II. In the following cases, identify the common medical emergency or injury and outline your response.

a. You are training a client, Tip Hoever, when 45 minutes into the session you begin to notice that Tip is starting to act as if he is under the influence of alcohol. He is trembling and has slurred speech and poor coordination. Tip complains that he is tired and has a severe headache. As he attempts to sit down, Tip falls backward and is lying on the floor unconscious.

b. You are about to meet your client for a training session when you notice he is stretching his calf muscle by placing one leg behind the other and pushing on a wall. Upon a second glance you notice that your client is actually pushing on a large window. As you walk over to warn him, the glass gives way and your client receives multiple cuts to his hands and wrists. As he turns, he holds up his wrists and screams in pain. He is bleeding profusely from his wrists. Blood gets on your hands, face and clothes.

continue on next page

Practice What You Know

Write out a diagnosis and action plan for the medical emergencies and injuries you are likely to encounter. You can use the information as a reference, to role play or to review as needed.

CHAPTER

17 Legal Guidelines and Professional Responsibilities

Getting Started

This chapter is designed to increase your comfort level with the legal issues related to personal training, and addresses some of the legal and business concerns you may have as a personal trainer. It summarizes your legal responsibility as a personal trainer and also describes the scope of practice of personal training. After completing this section you will have a better understanding of:

- the differences between independent contractors and employees
- the elements of a binding contract
- types of business structures available to personal trainers
- scope of practice
- legal responsibilities
- legal issues regarding liability, concepts and defense

Vocabulary

- independent contractor
- sole proprietorship
- general partnership
- limited partnership
- corporation
- scope of practice
- standard of care
- assumption of risk
- negligence
- defendant
- standard of care
- plaintiff
- risk management

Reading Assignment

Read Chapter 17 of the *ACE Personal Trainer Manual,* paying special attention to the words listed in the box to the left. After you have read the chapter, define these words on a separate piece of paper.

Expand Your Knowledge

I. Determine whether each of the following statements describe work conditions normally associated with either an independent contractor or an employee. Place a (C) next to the statements that meet the conditions for independent contractor status. Place an (E) next to the statements that meet the conditions for employee status.

_____ a. Payment is regularly made by the hour, not by the project.

_____ b. Time period for work is considered one week.

_____ c. Training is conducted using your own equipment.

_____ d. Training is provided for many businesses or clients.

_____ e. The facility provides continuing education and job training.

II. List the four elements necessary for a binding legal contract.

a. ______________________________

____

b. ______________________________

____

c. ______________________________

____

d. ______________________________

____

III. Determine whether the following benefits are most associated with either a sole proprietorship or a corporation. Place an (S) next to the statements that indicate a sole proprietorship benefit. Place a (C) next to the statements that indicate a corporation benefit.

_____ a. inexpensive and easy to form under the law

_____ b. separation of liability between personal and business acts

_____ c. owners, not businesses, are taxed

_____ d. minimal government regulation

IV. Select those statements you believe fall within the scope of practice of a personal trainer by marking them with an (X).

_____ a. using a health history form to prescribe treatment

_____ b. understanding a client's stress is due to a recent marital dispute

_____ c. recommending that your seemingly healthy client run for cardiovascular benefits

_____ d. advising your client to use antioxidants

V. For each of the following situations, describe how you could lower your risk of being found legally responsible if an injury occurred.

a. When a client complains that her new shoes hurt her feet, you say, "It takes a couple of workouts to break in a good pair of shoes."

____

____

____

b. While personal training at a health club, you notice that the clamps that keep the weights on the barbell are getting rusty and loose. You mention their condition to the fitness director, but continue to use them.

____

____

____

____

c. You are about to begin a 5-mile jog with a client when the client invites a neighbor to join you. The neighbor is not your client.

____

____

____

____

____

____

continued on next page

d. You receive new business cards, stating that you are a certified personal trainer and that you provide exercise prescriptions.

____

____

____

____

VI. Match the term on the left with its description on the right.

_____	a. risk management	1. a voluntary abandonment of the right to file suit
_____	b. negligence	2. demonstrates minimal competency
_____	c. standard of care	3. acknowledgment of inherent risk of activity
_____	d. certification	4. umbrella coverage
_____	e. informed consent	5. evaluating potential danger to client in order to reduce likelihood of injury
_____	f. riders	6. current industry performance levels
_____	g. waivers	7. failure to perform as a reasonable and prudent person

Show What You Know

I. List the main areas to evaluate when creating a risk management protocol.

II. Case Analysis: Analyze the following situation and describe: a) the argument the plaintiff would most likely pursue; b) the argument the defendant would most likely pursue; c) the rationale a judge might use to decide the case; and d) what could have been done to reduce the risk of liability.

Weeble vs. ReallyFit Personal Training Services

Robert Weeble, who is a client of ReallyFit Personal Training Services, dislocated his shoulder during a personal-training session with Doug Bunker at Mr. Weeble's home gym. Doug had asked Mr. Weeble to find something suitable to place under his heels for a squat exercise and Mr. Weeble found two pieces of wood glued together in his garage. Doug examined the wood, placed it on the floor, and said "This will do!" During the squat exercise, the wood came unglued and Mr. Weeble fell down and dislocated his shoulder.

Practice What You Know

Perform a risk-management assessment to evaluate the risk of hazards for your clients and your business.

Appendix A

Certification Information Guide

I. Purpose

The purpose of this information is to provide you with insight into the American Council on Exercise's (ACE) certification process. By understanding how the examination is developed, we believe you can better prepare for the exam. ACE follows the highest standards for professional and occupational certification tests, taking measures to uphold validity, reliability and fairness for all candidates in our examinations.

II. How is the Exam developed?

The ACE certification examinations are developed by ACE and volunteer committees of experts in the field(s) in cooperation with Columbia Assessment Services, Inc. (CAS), an independent testing agency. The exam development process involves the following steps:

A. Job Analysis

A committee of experts in the fitness field thoroughly analyzes the job requirements and develops an outline of the knowledge and skills necessary to perform the job competently.

B. Validation Study

A research survey is then conducted to determine if the job analysis is valid. This survey is sent to thousands of randomly selected fitness professionals for input and validation. The final outcome is the *Exam Content Outline*. (See Appendix B in the *ACE Personal Trainer Manual*).

C. Item Writing

A national panel of experts develops questions for the exam. Questions are tied specifically to the validated *Exam Content Outline,* which resulted from the job analysis. All questions are also referenced to an acceptable text or document and further validated for importance, criticality and relevance. CAS then reviews the questions for the degree to which they adhere to testing guidelines.

D. Exam Construction

The questions are then reviewed in detail one more time by the examination committee before being placed on the final exam forms.

E. Cut Score Determination

Once the final exam is constructed, the exam committee rates the difficulty of each question and the passing point is then determined by statistical analysis of the committee ratings. This analysis adjust for variability in the ratings and gives benefit to the test candidate.

F. Continual Exam Evaluation

Once the exam process is completed, continual evaluation and analysis of each question help to ensure validity. The examination is revised each year with items being reworked or replaced. Approximately every five years the exam-development process begins again with a new job analysis.

III. How is the Exam administered?

An independent testing agency is used to administer all ACE examinations to ensure exam security, integrity and the elimination of bias. Be assured that all of the policies that ACE follows concerning exam administration are required to maintain these high standards.

IV. Who is eligible to take the Exam?

Anyone who is at least 18 years of age and has a valid CPR certification is eligible to take the ACE certification exam. For the ACE Personal Trainer Certification Examination it is assumed that the examinee will be competent in the areas described in the *Exam Content Outline* found in Appendix B of the *ACE Personal Trainer Manual.* For information concerning fees, registration procedures and testing dates and sites, please contact ACE at the following address for an Exam Information Brochure.

American Council on Exercise
5820 Oberlin Drive, Suite 102
San Diego, CA 92121
(800) 825-3636

Appendix B

Answer Key

Chapter One: Exercise Physiology

Expand Your Knowledge

I. (a) 3, (b) 2, (c) 1, (d) 5, (e) 4

II. (a) 4, (b) 6, (c) 2, (d) 5, (e) 3, (f) 7, (g) 1

III. (a) Higher levels of testosterone in men cause greater hypertrophy and greater absolute strength gains. (b) Pulmonary circulation is limited to the heart and lungs while systemic circulation delivers blood to the rest of the body. (c) Aerobic energy systems utilize oxygen while anaerobic energy systems do not utilize oxygen. (d) Performance interval training is designed to enhance competitive performance while fitness interval training is designed to improve overall general fitness. (e) Slow-twitch muscle fibers or Type I fibers are red in color and have greater aerobic capacity while fast-twitch muscle fibers are white in color and have less aerobic capacity. (f) Cardiac muscle is found only in the heart and can grade the force of contraction while skeletal muscle is found throughout the body and only contracts maximally. (g) Immediate muscle soreness is believed to be caused by a build up in lactic acid while delayed onset muscle soreness is believed to be caused by small tears in the connective tissue surrounding the muscle and within the muscle itself.

IV. (a) I, (b) NC or D, (c) D, (d) D, (e) I

V. (a) depletion of ATP stores; (b) build up of lactic acid; (c) depletion of glycogen stores

VI. (a) 18 to 25 and 12 to 18; (b) muscle pump; (c) 50 and 100; (d) 50 and 85; (e) 60 to 90

VII. (1) the elastic limits of the ligaments and tendons crossing the joints; (2) the elasticity of the muscle tissue itself; (3) the bone and joint structure; (4) the skin

VIII. (a) D, (b) I, (c) I, (d) NC, (e) I, (f) I, (g) D

IX. cardiac output max = HR max x SV max (22,500 ml blood/min = 180 bpm x 125 ml/min);
VO_2 max = 48 ml O_2/kg/min or 3,600 ml O_2/min (3,600 ml O_2/min = 48 ml O_2/kg/min x 75 kg);
O_2 extraction max = VO_2 max/cardiac output max (16ml O_2/100 ml blood = 3,600 ml O_2/min ÷ 22,500 ml blood/min)

X. (1) Frequency = at least three times per week; (2) Intensity = 50% to 85% of maximum VO_2; (3) Type of exercise = rhythmic, large muscle movement; (4) Duration = at least 15 to 20 minutes per session

XI. First, there must be sufficient ATP near actin and myosin as well as a nervous impulse. Second, actin and myosin must link to form a cross bridge. Third, energy from ATP causes myosin to swivel. Fourth, actin is moved toward the center of the sarcomere causing the muscle fiber to shorten.

Show What You Know

I. Eileen has recruited previously inactive motor units and has increased the coordination of her motor units during her strength-training exercises. It is probably not due to muscle hypertrophy.

II. Anita may: (a) altitude: work at reduced levels until she becomes acclimatized, being cautious of symptoms of altitude sickness — headache, insomnia, irritability, weakness and dizziness; (b) heat: work at reduced levels to allow for elevated heart rate due to overheating, being careful to drink plenty of fluids, wear clothes that allow the sweat to dissipate heat, and sunscreen or protective clothing to avoid sunburn; (c) cold: wear layers of clothes that allow for adjustments due to changes in either body or environmental temperature. Clothing should allow the body to give off heat but keep moisture away from the skin. Make sure hands, feet and head stay warm. Maintain water intake regardless of temperature. Take special precautions in temperatures lower than 15°F (-9°C), avoid exercise in temperatures less than -15°F (-26°C).

Chapter Two: Human Anatomy

Expand Your Knowledge

I. (a) 6, (b) 2, (c) 5, (d) 1, (e) 4, (f) 8, (g) 7, (h) 3

II. (1) Carries carbon dioxide and metabolic waste from the cells. (2) Protects against disease. (3) Helps regulate body temperature. (4) Prevents serious blood loss after injury through the formation of clots

III. (a) Internal and external jugular veins; (b) Femoral artery; (c) Axillary artery; (d) Pulmonary vein; (e) Superior vena cava; (f) Renal artery

IV. (1) a, superior vena cava; (7) b, pulmonary vein; (2) c, right atrium; (4) d, semilunar valve; (3) e, right ventricle; (1) f, inferior vena cava; (11) g, aorta; (6) h, right and left pulmonary artery; (5) i, pulmonary trunk; (8) j, left atrium (9) k, mitral valve (10) l, left ventricle

V. (1) External respiration is the exchange of oxygen and carbon dioxide between the atmosphere and the large capillaries of the lungs. (2) Internal respiration involves the exchange of those gases between the blood and the cells of the body. (3) Cellular respiration involves the utilization of oxygen and the production of carbon dioxide by the metabolic activity of the cell.

VI. (a) 1, (b) 5, (c) 4, (d) 3, (e) 7, (f) 2, (g) 6, (h) 8

VII. (a) The central nervous system is completely enclosed in bone, such as the spinal cord and the brain, while the peripheral nervous system is connected to the extremities. (b) The axial skeleton is made up of the 80 bones of the head, neck and trunk, while the appendicular skeleton consists of the 126 bones that form the extremities. (c) Formed elements are living, such as red blood cells, while plasma is comprised of nonliving water and dissolved solutes. (d) Skeletal muscle contracts voluntarily, while cardiac and visceral muscle contract involuntarily. (e) Arteries carry blood away from the heart while veins carry blood toward the heart.

VIII. (a) Head, neck, upper chest and shoulders; (b) Shoulders down to the fingers of the hand; (c) Abdomen, groin, genitalia, and antero-lateral aspect of the thigh; (d) Large muscles of the posterior thigh, and the entire lower leg, ankle and foot

IX. (a) F, (b) I, (c) S, (d) L, (e) S, (f) F, (g) L, (h) L

X. (a) Have a space, or joint, between the bones that form them; a variety of movement can occur; (b) Have no joint cavity and are held together by cartilage; little or no motion occurs; (c) Have no joint cavity and are held tightly together by fibrous tissue; very little movement occurs

XI. (a) Saddle: flexion and extension; abduction and adduction; circumduction; opposition. (b) Ball and socket: flexion and extension; abduction and adduction; circumduction; internal and external rotation. (c) Modified hinge: flexion and extension; internal and external rotation. (d) Hinge: flexion and extension (e) Condyloid: flexion and extension; abduction and adduction; circumduction.

XII. see figures 2.17, 2.18, 2.19, 2.21, 2.23 and 2.27

Show What You Know

I. The "burning" feeling is a feedback mechanism that warns the body of possible injury if the current activity level is not reduced. It is the body's way of saying "slow down."

II. (a) Rectus femoris, vastus lateralis, intermedius and medialis; (b) Pectoralis major and latissimus dorsi; (c) External and internal obliques and rectus abdominus; (d) Peroneus brevis and longus, posterior tibialis, gastrocnemius and soleus; (e) Biceps brachii, brachioradialis, brachialis, flexor carpi radialis, flexor carpi ulnaris, pronator teres; (f) Rhomboid major and minor and trapezius

Chapter Three: Biomechanics and Applied Kinesiology

Expand Your Knowledge

I. Part 1: Gravity = MF, Biceps = RF
Part 2: Gravity = RF, Triceps = MF

II. In the first two classes of levers, the motive force is further away from the axis of rotation than the resistive force. The motive force of the third class lever is closer to the axis of rotation than the resistive force.

III. (a) 4, (b) 1, (c) 2, (d) 5, (e) 3

IV. (a) C, (b) P, (c) P, (d) P, (e) C, (f) A

V. (1) F, F; (2) S, C; (3) S, G; (4) T, A; (5) F, E; (6) M, B; (7) T, H; (8) F, D

VI. (1) Erector spinae, Rectus abdominus, External obliques, Internal obliques; (2) Gluteus medius and minimus; (3) Biceps femoris, Semitendinosus, Semimembranosus, Gracilis, Sartorius, and Gastrocnemeus; (4) Deltoid (middle), Supraspinatus; (5) Infraspinatus, Teres minor, and Deltoid (posterior); (6) Peroneus longus and Peroneus brevis; (7) Gluteus maximus, Biceps femoris, Semitendinosus and Semimembranosus; (8) Rhomboids, Levator scapulae and Trapezius (upper)

VII. Straighten arm to increase lever arm, increase weight, add manual resistance.

Show What You Know

I. One method is to place your hand on the back of Arnold's neck in the correct position, and help him hold this neutral position by maintaining contact throughout the exercise. Another method would be to place your hand in front of Arnold's forehead during the abdominal exercise. To maintain neutral position he must not touch your hand.

II. Although the chest group may be responsible for the joint action, the line of gravity is not in line with the weight movement. (Mary is not lifting or lowering the weights against the line of gravity.) An easy way to increase the effectiveness of this exercise would be to place Mary in the supine position on a bench and perform the same horizontal adduction and abduction.

Chapter Four: Nutrition

Expand Your Knowledge

I. Your body naturally produces nonessential nutrients, but does not produce essential nutrients. Essential nutrients must be acquired through the diet.

II. *See chart below.*

Major Classes of Nutrients	Recommended Intake	Primary Functions
Protein	12 to 20% of caloric intake	Builds and repairs tissue; major component of enzymes, hormones and antibodies
Carbohydrate	55 to 60% of caloric intake	Provides a major source of fuel to the body; provides dietary fiber
Lipids	25 to 30% of caloric intake	Energy storage in the body; insulate vital organs; provide fat-soluble vitamins
Vitamins	Listed in RDA	Aid reactions in the body; release energy in food
Minerals	Listed in RDA	Enable enzymes to function; a component of hormones; a part of bone and nerve
Water	2 to 3 quarts	Enables chemical reactions to occur; about 60% of body is water; essential for life

III. Low-density lipoproteins contain a greater amount of cholesterol and may be responsible for depositing cholesterol onto the artery walls. High-density lipoproteins are lower in cholesterol and aid in its removal from the cells.

IV. See page 120 of the *ACE Personal Trainer Manual* for the Food Guide Pyramid recommendations.

V. (a) calcium, protein and riboflavin; (b) protein, niacin, iron and thiamine; (c) vitamins A and C

VI. Lacto-ovo vegetarians eat milk and eggs but exclude fish, meat and poultry. Vegans do not eat any foods from animal sources.

VII. (1) Consume 1 to 2 cups of fluid at least one hour before the start of exercise. (2) Consume 4 to 10 ounces of fluid every 15 to 20 minutes during the workout. (3) Consume 2 cups of fluid for every pound of body weight lost after exercise.

VIII. (a) taste, (b) carbohydrate, (c) atherosclerosis, (d) green leafy vegetables, (e) hydrogenation

Show What You Know

I. Explain that athletes who eat a balanced diet of carbohydrates, fats and proteins have not shown any significant muscle gains from taking protein supplements. Using protein supplements can be expensive and dangerous to the body, particularly in large amounts, which can cause liver or kidney stress, dehydration, and loss of urinary calcium. Ask Anna what her goals are, what she has heard about protein supplements, and about her current diet. Assess whether her diet is balanced, or if the excess protein is taking the place of other valuable nutrients (especially sources of calcium like milk and milk products). Finally, explain to Anna that excess protein in the diet can be converted into fat.

II. Let Artie know that though his cholesterol levels are high, he may be able to lower them through a combination of diet and exercise. Explain the following:
• fats, especially those high in saturated fats, are linked with heart disease
• the process of atherosclerosis, and the role of cholesterol, LDL and HDL
• how exercise positively effects HDL and LDL • the food guide pyramid and the benefits of a well-balanced diet.
Ask Artie to identify the fat sources in his diet and use Table 4.8 on page 131 for fat substitutions. Finally, give Artie some general guidelines for a realistic nutritional program that he can adhere to.

Chapter Five: Health Screening

Expand Your Knowledge

I. (1) demographic information; (2) exercise history; (3) health risk factors; (4) medications; (5) recent and current illness and injuries; (6) surgery and illness history; (7) family medical history

II. (a) could be newly pregnant; (b) could still have a stress fracture; (e) many risk factors; (f) diabetic; (g) ACSM recommends any male older than 40 years of age obtain a complete physical before beginning an exercise program.

III. The healthcare professional must be degreed, licensed, boarded and/or otherwise qualified in their area of expertise. Also, it is important to recommend at least two professionals in order to avoid bias and to allow the client to make their own healthcare decisions.

Medications	Resting HR	Exercising HR	Maximal Exercising HR
Beta-adrenergic Blocking Agents	↓	↓	↓
Calcium Channel Blockers	↑ ←→ ↓	↑ ←→ ↓	←→
Caffeine	↑ ←→	↑ ←→	←→
Diuretics	←→	←→	←→
Antihypertensives	↑ ←→ ↓	↑ ←→ ↓	←→

IV. *See chart above.*

V. (a) A person with hyperthyroidism may have an already-high metabolic rate, and exercise may increase their metabolic rate to dangerously high levels. (b) The hernia may become worsened through lifting or improper breathing during moderate strength exercises. (c) Diuretics cause water loss and can cause cardiac dysrhythmias; exercise can increase this dehydrating effect. (d) In some people suffering from COPDs, exercise can lead to dyspnea.

VI. (a) 1, (b) 4, (c) 3, (d) 2

Show What You Know

I. (a) 5, (b) 3, (c) 2, (d) 1, (e) 4

II. Explain to Justin that you realize that he is frustrated because he wants to get started right away and he doesn't feel a physical is necessary. Then make it clear that the physical is for his own benefit (to find any risk factors before it's too late), and is a first step to getting started the right way. If you sense he objects because he is young, you may let him know that the physical he will undergo is like the physicals that most young sport stars undergo before they begin each season.

Chapter Six: Testing and Evaluation

Expand Your Knowledge

I. (1) cardiorespiratory efficiency; (2) muscular strength and endurance; (3) muscle and joint flexibility;

(4) body composition

II. (1) If the client has had no previous exercise experience; (2) If the client has had negative feelings or bad experiences with physical activity programs; (3) If the client has negative feelings or bad experiences with exercise testing; (4) If the client dislikes competitive experiences — specifically if they dislike being compared to others

III. (a) 70 and 75, (b) elevated, (c) 85, (d) .75, (e) up

IV. (a) Informs the client of the purpose, procedures, and possible negative side effects of the exercise testing, and may help you legally in the event that the client should suffer an injury or medical emergency as a result of the exercise testing. (b) Assists the tester in responding to a medical emergency, also may help you legally in the event that the client should suffer an injury or medical emergency as a result of the exercise testing. (c) Screens individuals at risk of a medical emergency as a result of exercise testing BEFORE they are tested.

V. (a) 3, (b) 7, (c) 6, (d) 1, (e) 8, (f) 9, (g) 2, (h) 4, (i) 5

VI. (a) Absolute does not factor in the weight of the individual while relative does factor in the weight of the individual. (b) Upper-body obesity indicates a higher health risk. (c) Muscular strength is the greatest amount of force that muscles can produce in a single maximal effort while muscular endurance is the muscle's ability to exert a submaximal force either repeatedly or statically over time. (d) The low-weight/high-repetition muscular endurance tests are more appropriate for less-fit clients and those clients that have health-related exercise-strength goals.

VII. (1) Do not go to stage II if the heart rate exceeds 140 at stage I; this person is unfit. (2) Stages IV and V should only be used for individuals under age 50. (3) Never go to the next stage if the heart rate exceeds 145 beats per minute.

VIII. (a) VO_2 MAX = 40.77 ml/min, CATEGORY = average; (b) VO_2 MAX = 35.52 ml/min, CATEGORY = above average; (c) VO_2 MAX = 29.72 ml/min, CATEGORY = below average; (d) poor

IX. (a) a diagonal skinfold taken midway on the anterior axillary line; (b) a vertical skinfold taken 1 inch lateral to the umbilicus; (c) a vertical fold on the back of the upper arm taken halfway between the acromion and olecranon processes; (d) a diagonal fold taken at, or just anterior to, the crest of the ilium

X. (a) **advantage**: dynamic movement that can be improved over time to show progress, easy to set up and administer; **disadvantage**: it uses a fixed weight, which places lighter clients at a disadvantage; (b) **advantage**: any strength test that involves movement will either underestimate or overestimate maximal force output due to internal friction, and easy to administer; **disadvantage**: most workouts will focus on dynamic strength training, so using this test for the purpose of establishing a baseline or to track progress may not be suitable; (c) **advantage**: easy to administer and to repeat; **disadvantage**: may cause muscle strain if performed too vigorously or when the client is not properly warmed up; (d) **advantage**: most accurate for most clients, especially when coupled with a residual volume measurement; **disadvantage**: can be expensive and time consuming, lack of availability, and may be inaccurate with clients uncomfortable with submersion in water

XI. (a) BMI = 22.5, CATEGORY = normal; (b) BODY FAT PERCENTAGE =15.6, CATEGORY = fitness; (c) BD = 1.022, BODY FAT PERCENTAGE = 34.3, CATEGORY = obese; (d) WTH RATIO = 0.810, CATEGORY = moderately high risk

XII. (a) Client has a shortness in the pectoralis major, teres major and latissimus dorsi area. (b) Client has below average trunk flexibility with severe lower back and hamstring inflexibility. (c) Fair rating of shoulder flexibility, lack of internal and external rotation. (d) Hip flexors are extremely tight.

XIII. (a) push-up test, bench-press test; (b) bent-knee curl-up test; (c) leg press

Show What You Know

I. (1) to establish a baseline to evaluate progress; (2) to establish goals and provide motivation; (3) to identify areas of health and injury risks; (4) to assist in developing an exercise program; (5) to assess current fitness levels relative to age and sex

II. 162 to 167 pounds

III. Bench press weight ratio = 1.78, CATEGORY = superior

Chapter Seven: Cardiorespiratory Fitness and Exercise

Expand Your Knowledge

I. Cardiovascular Health Benefits *(see Table 7.1)*; Adaptive Physiologic Responses *(see Table 7.1)*

II. (a) WU, (b) WU, (c) CD, (d) WU, (e) CD, (f) CD

III. (Case #1) b, (Case #2) a

IV. 6.6 - 7.7 METS (a) 7.0 Yes, (b) 9.0 No, (c) 4.1 No, (d) 8.7 No, (e) 7.2 Yes, (f) 8.3 No

V. (a) 114 - 133 bpm; (b) 146 - 157 bpm; (c) Karvonen is higher due to factoring in high resting heart rate.

VI. (a) 4 to 6; (b) 120 bpm

VII. Exercise to the point where you can still comfortably hold a conversation. If you are out of breath and can't hold a conversation, reduce the intensity.

VIII. (a) IM, (b) MA, (c) IN, (d) MA, (e) IN, (f) IM

IX. (a) The lower the initial level of fitness, the greater capacity or rate of improvement. (b) Age may effect exercise intensity; there is a slower rate of improvement at lower intensities.

(c) The longer the duration, the higher the rate of improvement up to a point. If exercise continues beyond that point, cardiovascular benefits may be reduced.

X. (a) INT, (b) AC, (c) FAR, (d) CIR, (e) CON

XI. Reasons to temporarily defer exercise *(see Table 7.12)*

XII. (a) decrease, (b) slightly bent, (c) lower, (d) are not, (e) wait 90 minutes, (f) anaerobic, (g) higher

Show What You Know

I. The four pulse sites: Carotid: first two fingers to Adam's apple, slide gently toward opposite side into groove. Temporal: place first two fingers to outside edge of eye brow, slide fingers up and back into soft spot. Radial: place first two fingers on wrist in line with the thumb, slide along wrist to groove. Apical: place two fingers below left clavicle, between the anterior deltoid and pectoralis major

II. Case study: Mode — Emma wants variety so add at least one new activity each 8-week session. Frequency — Emma needs consistency; try to get her to a solid 4 - 5x/week. Intensity — She first needs to begin monitoring intensity at around 60% of her maximum oxygen consumption and work up to near 70 percent. Duration — 30 minutes is fine for meeting criteria for improvement, it may be increased to try to reduce her body fat. Method — In order to create variety add at least one new method per 8-week period.

Chapter Eight: Muscular Strength and Endurance

Expand Your Knowledge

I. (a) **Advantages** include minimal equipment needed, low cost, space and time efficiency; **disadvantages** include blood pressure escalation, increases in strength only at specifically exercised positions in the movement range, training monotony and lack of performance feedback. (b) **Advantages** include accommodating resistance forces, speed regulation and detailed performance feedback; **disadvantages** include cost of equipment, inconsistent force regulation and lack of eccentric muscle contraction. (c) **Advantages** include low cost of equipment, similarity to most work and exercise activities, variety of training movements, evidence of improvement and easy accessibility; **disadvantages** include the inability to train through a full range of joint motion in some exercises, and inconsistent matching of resistive forces throughout the exercise movements. (d) **Advantages** include the ability to train through a full range of joint motion on most exercises, reasonably consistent matching of resistive forces throughout the exercise movements and, in most cases, tangible evidence of improvement; **disadvantages** include equipment expense, limited number of training movements and lack of accessibility.

II. (1) C, (2) F, (3) A, (4) D, (5) G, (6) B, (7) E, (8) H

III. (a) increased capacity to perform work; (b) enhances physical appearance and prevents loss of lean tissue that normally accompanies the aging process; (c) increases resting metabolic rate preventing excess energy storage as fat; (d) reduces risk of injury and many degenerative diseases

IV. 84 pounds

V. (1) all; (2) a and b

VI. Type I fibers are slow-twitch, fatigue slowly and are better suited for aerobic or endurance activities, while Type II fibers are fast-twitch, fatigue quickly and are better suited for anaerobic activities.

Show What You Know

I. (a) 85 pounds, (b) 80 pounds, (c) 75 pounds, (d) 70 pounds

II. The process of strength training results in microscopic tears to the muscle and connective tissue. The body usually requires 24 to 48 hours to fully recover so that strengthening can occur. If workouts are too close together, the body will not have a chance to fully recover and build strength.

Chapter Nine: Strength Training Program Design

Expand Your Knowledge

I. What are your short- and long-term goals? What types of performance improvements (for example, activities or sports your client participates in) would you like to see? Is the training dictated by the needs of the individual or the requirements of the sport? How much time would you like to commit?

II. (a) B, (b) F, (c) C, (d) H

III. Asking Anita to do heavy work during her rest will probably not keep her motivated. Instead, use light stretching, abdominal and low-back exercises, a brisk walk to the water fountain, or work small muscle groups of the lower body such as the calves.

IV. (a) 4 weeks, (b) volume, (c) four to five seconds, (d) 12 to 20 repetitions

V. (a) Janet is just getting started so she has a lower percentage of her 1RM, while John is a seasoned exerciser who has a strength-gain goal. (b) John requires more rest and recovery because his intensity is greater per lift. (c) John is training for two exercises — the "clean and jerk" and the "snatch" — so his number of exercises is limited. Janet's goal is total body fitness so she challenges all her major muscle groups.

VI. (a) 2, (b) 4, (c) 5, (d) 3, (e) 1, (f) 3, (g) 4

VII. Record repetitions, sets, resistance, order of exercises, name of exercise and periodization planning program.

Loading	Outcome	%1RM	Rep Range	# of sets	Rest
Light	muscular endurance	<70	12-20	1-3	20-30 seconds
Moderate	hypertrophy, strength	70-80	8-12	1-6	30-120 seconds
Heavy	maximum strength/power	80-100	1-8	1-5+	2-5 minutes

VIII. *See chart above.*

IX. 1. Use a progressive increase in resistance over time. 2. Cause the targeted muscles to fatigue in about 30 to 90 seconds. 3. Challenge all the major muscle groups.

Show What You Know

I. Ask Rita how much time she has to devote to a complete exercise program and other questions that will help you establish long term goals. Let Rita know that drop-out rates are higher with new exercisers who begin at too high of a frequency and that training two times per week produces up to 80 percent of the benefits of training three times a week. Let her know she can gradually increase her frequency as her body adapts to her new strength-training program.

II. See exercise descriptions from Chapter 9 of the *ACE Personal Trainer Manual.*

Chapter Ten: Flexibility

Expand Your Knowledge

I. Increased physical efficiency and performance; decreased risk of injury; increased blood supply and nutrients to joint structures; may increase the quantity and decrease the thickness of synovial fluid, increased neuromuscular coordination; improved muscular balance and postural awareness; decreases low back pain; reduced stress and enhanced enjoyment

II. (a) 4, (b) 2, (c) 5, (d) 3, (e) 1

III. (a) During a passive stretch the contractile components of the muscle are relaxed; during an active stretch the muscles are contracting through the range of motion. (b) Static flexibility does not emphasize movement while dynamic flexibility involves speed, strength and control. (c) During an elastic stretch the tissues elongate, but recover when the tension is removed; during a plastic stretch the deformation to the tissue remains after the tension is removed. (d) Pre-exercise stretching is primarily active and is aimed at reducing muscle stiffness; post-exercise stretching is for permanent increases in flexibility. (e) Low-force, long-duration stretching promotes greater plastic change.

IV. (a) a slow, gradual and controlled elongation through a full range of motion; (b) a high-force, short duration method that employs rapid, uncontrolled bouncing motions; (c) a method of promoting the response of neuromuscular mechanisms through the stimulation of proprioceptors in an attempt to gain more stretch in a muscle

V. (a) WU, (b) CD, (c) CD, (d) WU, (e) WU, (f) CD

VI. (a) The greatest increases in flexibility occur between the ages of seven and 12. After adolescence, flexibility tends to decline with an acceleration in flexibility loss that begins at age 25. The age-related effect strengthens connective tissue bonds, creating increased resistance to deformation. Activity also plays a role in maintaining flexibility, given that people tend to become less active as they age. This inactivity also contributes to decreasing flexibility during the aging process. (b) Females are more flexible than males, which may be a genetic factor that is related to the flexibility necessary to accommodate childbirth. (c) There is little or no evidence that body type affects range of motion. (d) As muscles become warm, they become more pliable. Cold muscles may be injured by intense stretching.

VII. genetic inheritance; the joint structure itself; connective tissue elasticity within the muscles, tendons or skin surrounding the joint; connective tissue elasticity within muscles; strength of the opposing muscle groups; and neuromuscular coordination

Show What You Know

I. (a) See figure 10.22a; (b) See figure 10.22b; (c) See figure 10.20; (d) See figure 10.21; (e) See figure 10.11

II. (a) slow and controlled; (b) light kicks; (c) lie supine, guide leg up while stabilizing pelvis, push against resistance, release

Chapter Eleven: Programming for the Healthy Adult

Expand Your Knowledge

I. (1) medical/health screening; (2) physical fitness testing; (3) selection of exercise mode; (4) design of an exercise program for total fitness

II. Asking sedentary individuals to adopt a vigorous exercise plan has not been successful in motivating people to commit to a healthy lifestyle — it is too big of a change. The exercise lite guidelines are to help encourage sedentary individuals to improve their overall health by adding light to moderate activities to their weekly schedules.

III. (a) 5, (b) 4, (c) 1, (d) 6, (e) 7, (f) 3, (g) 2

IV. (a) 6, (b) 4, (c) 1, (d) 3, (e) 7, (f) 2, (g) 5

V. (a) typically lasts 4 to 6 weeks, intensity, frequency and duration are at lower end of training range; increases are gradual; (b) usually lasts 12 to 20 weeks; frequency, intensity and duration are at the middle of the training range; retesting fitness components every 3 months; (c) usually begins 5 to 6 months after beginning an exercise program; variety and convenience are the keys to keeping client motivated

VI. (a) Because the client is sedentary at home and work, it is better to begin slowly to allow the client to adapt to a new habit of exercising — this is the key to long-term success. At the same time, she was medically cleared and will want to see results, so a moderate intensity is recommended. (b) Bicycling and rowing have a muscular strength endurance rating of 3 and 4, respectively, while walking and running have a muscular strength and endurance rating of 2. Because the client has a primary strength-training/weight-gain goal, rowing and bicycling are better suited.
(c) In this case, the physician has recommended a slow progression, so the intensity of 40 to 50 percent is recommended.

VII. (a) 75,000, (b) "lack of time", (c) 30, (d) half

Show What You Know

I. Walking has been shown to have a high compliance because it is easy and convenient. It requires minimal skill and equipment, and can be done by people of all ages, alone or in groups.

II. There are no health limitations noted. Since his goal is to cross train, find out what other modes of cardiovascular exercise he would be interested in. Even though he has a high to average fitness level, introducing a new mode of aerobic exercise will cause soreness if it is too intense. Start by changing one of his three days per week to a new activity, beginning at a lower intensity to avoid soreness and injury. Look at ways to make easy changes in his weight-training program. For example, exercise major muscle groups with different machines or exercises, change one set into two sets for major muscle groups and change either number of reps for the second set. Finally, emphasize a more regimented flexibility program to increase flexibility.

Chapter Twelve: Special Populations and Health Concerns

Expand Your Knowledge

I. (a) D, (b) I, (c) D, (d) D, (e) D

II. 3. Aerobic endurance and weight training in combination has shown to be the most effective way to contribute to a weight-management program. The combination burns calories and stimulates muscle/metabolic rate.

III. (a) 1, 2, 3, 4, 5, (b) 4, 5, (c) 4, 5, (d) 1, (e) 2

IV. unsupported forward flexion; twisting at the waist with turned feet, especially when carrying a load; lifting both legs simultaneously while in the prone or supine position; rapid movements such as twisting, forward flexion and hyperextending

V. (a) 40 percent to 75 percent heart rate reserve; (b) gradually increased to 20 to 30 minutes; (c) three to four nonconsecutive days per week

VI. (a) 3, (b) 1, (c) 2, (d) 3, (e) 1, (f) 1

VII. (a) Bronchitis is an inflammation of the bronchial tubes, while emphysema is caused by over-inflation of the alveoli.
(b) Osteoarthritis is a degenerative disease of the joint cartilage while rheumatoid arthritis is an inflammation of the membrane surrounding the joint.
(c) Insulin-dependent diabetes mellitus (IDDM) is caused by the destruction of insulin producing cells, which occurs in childhood, while non-insulin-dependent diabetes mellitus (NIDDM) usually occurs during adulthood in overweight individuals and is characterized by a decreased sensitivity to insulin.
(d) CVA affects the arteries of the nervous system instead of the heart.

VIII. jumping, high impact aerobics, jogging and running; spinal flexion, crunches and rowing machines; trampolines and step aerobics; abducting or adducting their legs against resistance; moving their legs sideways across their body; pulling on their neck with their hands behind their head

Show What You Know

I. An example might be: (a) reduce outdoor ride to 60 minutes at reduced intensity; (b) change high-impact to low-impact to reduce impact, and cycle indoors in air-conditioned environment; (c) reduce-low impact aerobics from 3x/week to 2x/week and cycle only 45 minutes.

II. (a) sustained activities like walking, swimming; (b) will use perceived exertion scale starting low and working up to high-moderate; (c) two to three days of cardiovascular training; (d) gradually increase to 30 to 40 minutes; (e) can be done safely if Ima wants to strength train; recommend performing 10 strength exercises 2 times/week at 12 to 15 repetitions to start.

Chapter Thirteen: Principles of Adherence and Motivation

Expand Your Knowledge

I. (a) PRO, (b) PER, (c) PER, (d) ENV, (e) ENV

II. First, let the client know you are there — a brief supportive, non-judgmental telephone call. Second, encourage the client to return to their exercise regime as soon as possible.

III. (a) Your dress, behavior and demeanor, as well as respecting the client-trainer relationship, and the client's privacy and confidentiality; (b) Placing effort and extra work into all aspects of the workout, staying current and finding answers to client's concerns and questions;
(c) Recognizing and understanding each client for their unique situation, and giving and receiving feedback;
(d) Taking active steps to prevent burnout: seeking advice of others, set-

ting goals, time off, and soliciting support from others; (e) Being prepared for each session, starting and ending the sessions on time, and arranging for substitutes when unable to attend

IV. (a) 50 percent or more, (b) musculoskeletal injury, (c) 9 percent, (d) critical period

V. When a personal trainer does not recognize that there are more than just personal factors influencing a client's motivation to exercise, they sometimes blame the client for the failure. Instead, a personal trainer should view motivation as a joint responsibility. Motivation is dynamic and changes with each client and through different stages of the program.

VI. stiffness, minor soreness or muscle pain and fatigue

Show What You Know

I. Modify Joe's exercise program to make it less physically challenging. Modify the program to include small breaks or decrease the intensity of the exercises. Also, emphasize the physical and mental health benefits of Joe's new program.

II. Short-term benefits include: feelings of accomplishment, stress reduction, better sleep and circumference changes in arms and legs. Emphasize short-term benefits when the client becomes discouraged about meeting the long-range goals or the immediate discomfort of exercise does not seem to be paying off for them.

Chapter Fourteen: Communication and Teaching Techniques

Expand Your Knowledge

I. (a) I, (b) A, (c) R, (d) P

II. (a) 2, (b) 6, (c) 4, (d) 5, (e) 3, (f) 1

III. (a) Needs to be measurable and more time-bound: I want to maintain a weight of 165 pounds through the months of November, December and January.
(b) This will most likely be unhealthy or difficult to attain: I want to lose 15 pounds in three months. (c) Needs to be measurable and time-bound: I want to attain 18 percent body fat by April 30th.

IV. (a) A, (b) K, (c) V, (d) K, (e) V, (f) A

V. The first part specifies the behavior to be achieved. The second part specifies the reinforcements that will reward the behavior.

VI. (a) What is your impression of today's workout? (b) How have you been using your food diary? (c) What type of workout did you have in mind today?

VII. (1) it is specific; (2) it is dependent on performance; (3) it provides corrective information

Show What You Know

I. Tell — Explain the benefits of a proper cool-down (decreases residual muscle soreness, increased flexibility, reduced likelihood of injury) and dangers of improper cool-downs (blood pooling and stress on the cardiovascular system).
Show — Demonstrate by reducing the jog to a fast walk and then to a slow walk. Demonstrate stretches that can be used at the end of the session (calf stretches, hamstring, hip flexors, quadriceps, etc.)
Do — Observe Max during the end of his run, and give him positive feedback as he properly cools down. Offer constructive feedback when he does not perform the cool-down properly.

II. (a) Max may display angry, frowning, grimacing or distracted facial expressions, pursed lips, rigid or backward-leaning body posture, crossed arms, foot tapping and crossed legs.
(b) What is it you dislike about cool-downs? What is your reaction to my suggestion to cool down? What are your thoughts or feelings about my suggestion to cool down? I am sensing you do not like to cool down; what are some of the reasons?
(c) Well, Max, today we worked on a cool-down that takes a minimal amount of time and increases the benefits of your exercise program. I showed you the steps to the cool-down and gave you a chance to practice it on your own. You brought the intensity down at a safe rate and stretched the most important muscle groups. At the end you said you felt better after the cool-down — more refreshed and ready for the rest of your day. It sounds like we both enjoyed the session.

Chapter Fifteen: Musculoskeletal Injuries

Expand Your Knowledge

I. (a) L, (b) T, (c) M, (d) B (e) B

II. (a) Stop exercising, remove the client from the hot environmental conditions and, if he's conscious, give fluids.
(b) Remove the client from the cold environment, warm them as quickly and gently as possible and, if they are conscious, give them warm fluids.

III. (1) E, (2) G, (3) B, (4) D, (5) A, (6) C, (7) F

IV. R = Rest — Avoid continuing the activity that caused the injury.
I = Ice — Apply ice for 20 to 30 minutes and insulate the area.
C = Compression — Apply elastic bandages to the injured area.
E = Elevation — Raise the injury to the height of the heart or higher.

V. (1) increased temperature, (2) redness, (3) swelling, (4) pain, (5) loss of function

Show What You Know

I. (a) Ideally, use a machine that does not require a hand grip, or in some cases, chest flyes will work because there is not as much stress on the wrist.
(b) Suggest any activity that reduces impact forces on the lower leg, for example walking or swimming. (c) Advise the client to drink plenty of water, run early or late in the day when it is cooler, or run or walk in an air-conditioned environment.

II. If you are not a practicing physician, you

must refer the client to a physician for diagnosis and prescription. If the physician diagnoses it as a stress fracture, you can communicate with the physician to create alternative exercises to Sue's current program. The physician may recommend exercises that minimize impact forces on the lower leg, such as light cycling on a stationary bike.

Chapter Sixteen: Emergency Procedures

Expand Your Knowledge

I. CPR micro shield or pocket mask, sphygmomanometer, stethoscope, penlight or flashlight, personal protective equipment, sterile gauze dressing, adhesive tape, bandage, scissors, liquid soap, splinting material and chemical cold pack.

II. Any of the following steps: a) protect the spine if a fall has occurred; b) check the head and face; c) perform a more thorough neurological exam; d) look at the skin; e) observe the chest for injury; f) look at the victim's general appearance; g) check vital signs; h) ask whether the victim has abdominal pain; i) check for injury to arms and legs

III. (1) The aura — when an unusual sensation warns the person that a seizure is imminent. (2) The tonic phase — the victim loses consciousness, holds their breath, and is rigid. (3) The clonic phase — the muscles alternate between relaxed and contracted. (4) The postictal phase — the victim is confused or comatose and the tonic/clonic activity ceases.

IV. (a) Emergency medical technicians (EMTs) are trained to administer basic care, while paramedics are trained to administer advanced care for life-threatening emergency needs. (b) Primary assessment identifies any threats to life or limb, while secondary assessment occurs once the life-threatening needs of the victim have been addressed. (c) Angina is chest pain that does not cause permanent damage, while a myocardial infarction results in permanent damage to the myocardium. (d) A simple (closed) fracture does not puncture the skin. A compound (open) fracture results in part of the bone piercing through the skin, or occurs when a sharp object penetrates the skin and fractures the underlying bone.
(e) Sprains are tears of the ligaments, while muscle strains can be microscopic or gross and are located at the muscle or tendon.

V. (a) 1, (b) 3, (c) 2, (d) 6, (e) 7, (f) 4, (g) 5

VI. (1) assess the airway using C-spine precautions if indicated; (2) look to see whether the victim's chest rises and falls; (3) after two breaths, check the victim's circulation by checking the carotid pulse; (4) look quickly for signs of bleeding and control hemorrhage with direct pressure over the wound; (5) perform a rapid neurologic exam

VII. A = airway, B = breathing, C = circulation. Because the brain needs oxygen it is most important to make sure that oxygen can first get into the lungs, then circulated to the brain. Circulating blood that doesn't contain oxygen is ineffective.

Show What You Know

I. (1) Due to increased energy utilization, her insulin dose may need to be adjusted as she begins to exercise. (2) Give her a list of potentially steady-state exercises (walking, cycling) so she can get approval for a variety of exercises. (3) Have the doctor review when and where insulin injections should be administered to avoid injecting insulin at the wrong time in the wrong place. (4) Have the doctor suggest an energy source (amount and frequency) to take during exercise. (5) pre-exercise eating, (6) methods for monitoring her blood sugar levels on her own, or may need to monitor herself more frequently

II. (a) Tip is most likely having a hypoglycemic reaction. (1) Check the airway, breathing and circulation. (2) Activate the EMS System. (3) Protect the victim and prevent injury in case they have a seizure. (4) Do not give anything by mouth. (b) First, activate the EMS (dial 911). Attempt to place a barrier between you and any wounds or blood by wearing rubber gloves or grabbing a towel or shirt. Next, apply direct pressure to the wounds and elevate the arms above the heart. If others are available, ask if they can obtain rubber gloves, or another barrier so they can apply pressure to the wounds or to other pressure points at the brachial site. Do not apply a tourniquet as pressure and elevation should stop the bleeding until help arrives. Try to get the victim to calm down through reassurance. Help the paramedics when they arrive. Because you have been showered with blood, you need to wash your entire body with soap and running water. Any objects that have come in contact with blood (glass, clothes) must be contained and properly washed or disposed of.

Chapter Seventeen: Legal Guidelines and Professional Responsibilities

Expand Your Knowledge

I. (a) E, (b) C, (c) C, (d) C, (e) E

II. (a) an offer and acceptance with mutual agreement of terms; (b) consideration — an exchange of valuable items, such as money for services; (c) legality — acceptable form under the law; (d) ability of the parties to enter into a contract with respect to legal age and mental capabilities

III. (a) S, (b) C, (c) S, (d) S

IV. (b) X, (c) X

V. (a) Point out to the client that the shoes may not be right for her, and that quality fitness shoes should not require a break-in period. (b) Stop using worn, frayed or potentially dangerous equipment. Instead of a verbal statement, express your concern in writing and keep a copy for your files. (c) Do not allow the neighbor to join in on the run this time. After a health-history screening, a waiver of liability and, in some cases, physician's approval have been obtained, the neighbor would be able to join if the 5-mile run was within their ability. (d) Do not use these cards unless you are a licensed doctor. Change "exercise prescriptions" to "exercise programs."

VI. (a) 5, (b) 7, (c) 6, (d) 2, (e) 3, (f) 4, (g) 1

Show What You Know

I. instruction, supervision, facilities, equipment, contracts and business structure

II. (a) Argument for the plaintiff — In this case, the plaintiff will probably choose to focus on the point of law known as negligence. Mr. Weeble will try to establish that Doug should not have approved the two pieces of glued wood for suitable workout equipment. The plaintiff also will try to establish that placing a piece of wood under his heels is not within the standard of care. The plaintiff also may site the *ACE Personal Trainer Manual,* which offers spotting tips for quadriceps exercises performed from a standing squat position. Chapter 9, page 282, reads, "Avoid use of board under heels." The plaintiff will then try to establish that he has indeed suffered an injury, and that the improper material and exercise recommendation led to the injury.

(b) Argument for the defendant — In this case, the defendant would try to establish that the plaintiff knew the inherent risks of the exercise prior to the accident, and that the plaintiff selected the piece of wood knowing it would be placed under the heels during the exercise.

(c) The judge would probably settle the case in favor of the plaintiff because it would seem that the defendant had a duty to properly supervise the plaintiff's workouts, which he did not fulfill. Also, the injury that was sustained was directly caused by the improper use of equipment and exercise recommendation by the defendant.

(d) Avoid the use of homemade props or equipment, and don't place objects under the heels during standing squats.